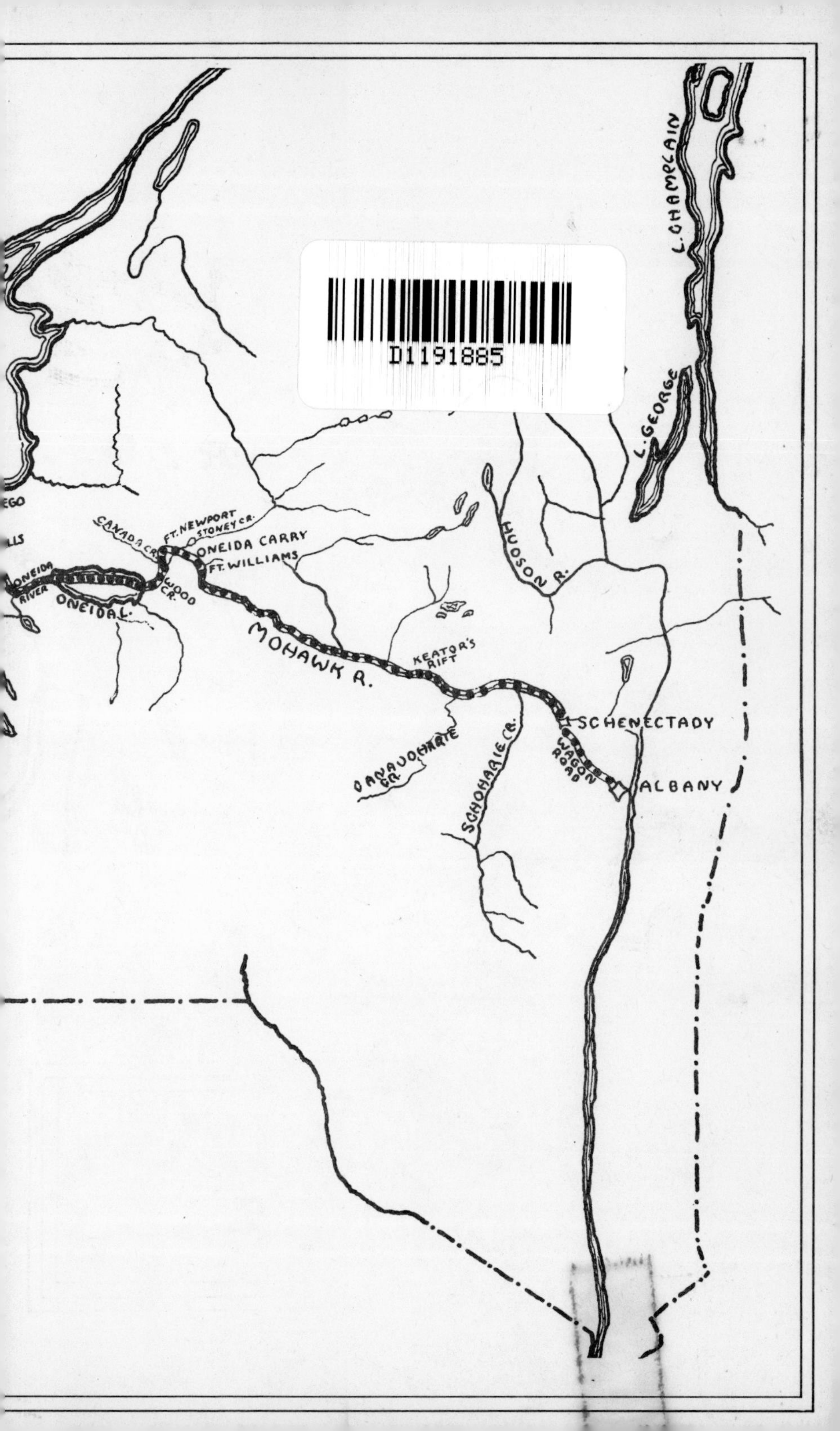

L. CHAMPLAIN
L. GEORGE
HUDSON R.
CANADA CR.
FT. NEWPORT
STONEY CR.
ONEIDA CARRY
FT. WILLIAMS
ONEIDA RIVER
ONEIDA L.
WOOD CR.
MOHAWK R.
KEATOR'S RIFT
SCHENECTADY
WAGON ROAD
ALBANY
CANAJOHARIE CR.
SCHOHARIE CR.

The Birth of the Erie Canal

OTHER BOOKS BY HARVEY CHALMERS II

West to the Setting Sun, 1943

Drums Against Frontenac, 1949

Joseph Brandt: Mohawk, 1955

THE BIRTH OF THE ERIE CANAL

by

HARVEY CHALMERS II

With the Collaboration of
John H. Flandreau

BOOKMAN ASSOCIATES :: New York

Library of Congress Catalog Card Number: 60-53229

TECHNICAL ASSISTANCE AND LAYOUT BY JOHN LATIMER MOORE
END PAPERS BY DON NEGUS

MANUFACTURED IN THE UNITED STATES OF AMERICA BY
UNITED PRINTING SERVICES, INC.
NEW HAVEN, CONN.

FOR RUTH BROWN EYES DANCING

FOREWORD

Each generation must face its own peculiar set of problems and challenges. Progress is the product of a partnership of bold imagination, undaunted conviction and forthright action. This has been true in every age and for every generation.

Today we are faced with the intricacies of supersonic travel and the imponderables of space exploration. A hundred-or-so years ago, there was the problem of powered land transportation—and so on back through history. The problem may change but the forces motivating man remain the same. The same qualities of character which will bring about the exploration of outer space and the colonization of the moon have, in the past, moved men to stretch their imaginations and charter bold new enterprises. This has been the story of the United States, and it is through the eyes of history that we gain some of the inspiration and confidence that can help us meet today's complex demands.

Improvements in transportation have helped measure and push forward the stages of our growth in wealth and power. Just as there was a particular significance to Roman roads in ancient times, so in New York's past, the development of our waterways marked the beginning of an unparalleled period of prosperity. This prosperity began with the completion of the Erie Canal, which was, however, only an outward symbol. Of deeper significance is the story of the men who through intrigue and imagination, mercenary schemes and patriotic dreams, personal plans and political ambitions brought meaning and substance to hopes and speculations. The vision of these men, who thought their way across

New York State by water, brought meaning to the appellation "the Empire State."

This book is not only part of the story of American progress, but also an intimate view of a critical period in New York's history. It is probable that a cross-State canal would have been built even if the principal characters in this book had never been born. However, other men would have played the roles differently—at different times and with different impact. It was an era of critical balance; an era in which long shadows were cast on the future; an era in which the antecedents of our present political, social and economic situation were established; an era which molded the primacy of the Empire State. For these reasons alone Harvey Chalmers' story is of unusual interest.

There are, however, other considerations which, perhaps, will annoy the historian but delight the reading public. Mr. Chalmers' story of the "Birth of the Erie Canal" is neither fact nor fiction but an unusual and cleverly interwoven combination of that which we know and that which we surmise. There is in this book a quality of imaginative realism which undergirds the author's interpretation and extension of known historical facts. Time tends to take the edge off of facts and each historian molds some of himself into the record. The storytelling technique which Mr. Chalmers employs in welding fact and fiction lends itself particularly well to the expression of his personal views. These may well be in conflict with popular conceptions, but honesty is a redeeming virtue and may in part justify his frank approach. Particularly in the light of the primary sources, the readability of this account and the author's genuine sincerity leave a lasting impression.

Hugh M. Flick, Ph.D.

Slingerlands, New York
September 10, 1960

ACKNOWLEDGMENT

The writer wishes to acknowledge with thanks the comments and criticism of Richard N. Wright, President of Onondaga Historical Association at Syracuse, New York.

CONTENTS

ILLUSTRATIONS

JONAS PLATT

"Iustum et tenacem propositi virum
Non civium ardor prava iubentium
non voltus instantis tyranni mente
quatit solida . . ."

He that is just and firm of will
quakes not before the fury of
mobs that instigate to ill, nor
can the tyrant's menace shake
his fixed resolve . . .

Horace, Odes III, iii, "Apotheosis of Romulus"
(after a translation by Theodore Martin)

(*Author's Note: The Latin quotation is said, by one of Jonas Platt's descendants, to have been affixed to the back of a portrait of Judge Platt, hanging in Albany. All efforts to locate this portrait have failed.)*

CHAPTER ONE

RETURN OF THE WILDERNESS

In the autumn of 1783, the red gods had decked the forest leaves with brilliant paints and sent many of them as peace offerings floating on the swift shallow current of the Mohawk River. In the valleys of the Hudson and the Mohawk the Indian war drums and the kettledrums of the British were silent. From the charred timbers of ruined Fort Stanwix and the sagging, deserted palisade of Fort Schuyler to the villages of the Americans at Schenectady and Albany, only the eerie drumming of the ruffed grouse broke the silence.

The leaves fell and snow covered the skeletons at Oriskany, the blackened open frames that had been houses, and the lonely chimneys. Ice hushed the river's murmuring rifts. There was stillness—the white silence of the wilderness and of desolation. The warriors of the Five Nations had fled toward the setting sun, never again to return and with their red belts to bind the disunited American colonists into bands of brothers. The Valley of the Mohawk was as it had been before the gay calls of the red people and the ring of the axes of the dirt-grubbing white men had awakened its echoes.

But late in May of 1784, when the ice and freshets had gone and birds again jewelled the trees, the black noses of two heavily laden bateaux appeared at the rift below German Flatts. They were poled by a big, harsh-faced Yankee from Middletown, Connecticut, named Hugh White and three of his sons. On the rutted, swampy road along the south bank of the river, White's fourth son kept pace driving a yoke of oxen hitched to a cart.

Believing that the New York frontier at Sauquoit Creek was too untamed for a white woman, Mrs. White had remained in Connecticut. Not until they had built a home in which she could live with security and a degree of comfort would she attempt to join them.

The sun had risen when the bateaux reached the first rift above the confluence of West Canada Creek. White, in the leading boat, poled into the backwater at the foot of the rift and studied the current. Since passing the mouth of Schoharie Creek, the river had narrowed and the flow had shallowed. It had become a swift stream sliding over its bed of slippery stones. White could see in the rift only one slick where the water was deep enough to float their boats. A low stone wall extended downstream at an angle from either bank in the form of a funnel. Squeezed into this narrow opening the water's depth was sufficient to float their laden bateaux, if they could pole them through without veering.

White shouted to his two other sons to let their boat drift down far enough to get a good start, as he was then doing. At the proper moment he set his pole and gave a mighty shove, seconded by his son. Strongly propelled, but without practiced timing, the bateau glided unevenly up through the mouth of the funnel, losing momentum as it neared the head of the rift where the current was swiftest. There, with the bow projecting out of water above the lip of the rift, progress ended.

White and his son, equally inexperienced in swift water poling, jabbed and heaved, but the mossy stones rolled under their iron-tipped poles. They churned the water white, their foreheads glistening in the morning sun. Inch by inch the bow passed the lip of the rift and hovered a moment over the smooth water of the level ahead. It was their strength against the river. Then, slowly, the force of the current, like an unseen hand drew them back downstream. But they were able to keep the bow of the boat headed upstream until well below the funnel. Suddenly the tip of White's pole glanced from a rounded stone. Instantly, the swells careened the boat until water slopped over the gunwales. Stooping, White grabbed a heavy sack of seed corn and lifted it out of the bilge surging across the keel. His son, using his pole as a rudder, steered the boat into quiet water a hundred yards downstream. Together they poled the boat up to the eddy-washed pebbled beach where the other sons were waiting. They were grinning. Unconcerned about their father's safety, they wanted to know whether the seed corn was still dry.

White reproved them in his usual ponderous manner. "My boys, if the boat had capsized and we had lost the seed corn, I'd have to return to Schenectady—or perhaps even Albany—to buy another supply." White steadied the bateau with his pole, scowling at the racing current.

The boy at the stern tactfully suggested that they unload both bateaux, drag them, one by one, up the rift by a rope and reload them in the calm water above.

White reluctantly agreed, handed an end of a rope to the two largest boys and ordered them to go above the rift, wade out into the deepest water and haul on the rope for dear life. Meanwhile, he attached the other end to the bow of the boat. When the boys were ready White and his son forced the boat up through the rift quite easily and safely beached it. The boy who had suggested the rope method then remarked in a highly disgruntled manner that, though feasible, it was a Hell of a way to handle a boat.

Without a word of appreciation for the suggestion White sternly rebuked his son for his vainglory and blasphemy.

After letting that sink in, White reminded them that he was due at the mouth of Sauquoit Creek in the Sedaqueda Patent by the fifth of June as that was the appointed time and place where he and his three partners, Zephaniah Platt,

Melancthon Smith, and Ezra L'Homidieu were to meet and divide the Patent by lot. Surveyors had measured the Patent into four tracts. They had agreed to draw for choice. Any partner who might arrive too late for the drawing would, according to agreement, take what was left. White roared to the boys in the second bateau to stop gaping and come on. They still had more than twenty-five miles of even narrower and swifter river ahead of them. Furthermore, the ox-cart had caught up, but was stuck in the mud. In a moment the driver would be calling for help.

As before, two of the boys waded waist-deep above the head of the rift, but this time their groping feet failed to find big bottom stones against which they could brace themselves. The smaller stones rolled under their shoes affording an insecure foothold. As they took up the slack of the rope, they saw that they were barely keeping the boat pointed upstream and certainly not pulling it ahead. The thrusts of White and his son were powerful but, as before, lacked the timing and rhythm of professional bateaumen. The bateau moved jerkily up the rift. The bow passed the lip, paused, inched ahead, then lost a little. From the brush on the south bank came a despairing yelp. White called back "Whassa matter?"

His fourth son shouted, "The cart's sinking in a mud hole. I'm pushing the wheel and I'm sinking too, damn it! Help!"

White roared "Don't curse—pray! We'll be there as soon as we can."

Involuntarily, the boys hauling on the rope turned their heads. White missed a stroke. The bateau swung sidewise, capsized and bumped downstream over the stones dragging the boys on the rope after it.

It was well past noon when the bateau was emptied of water and reloaded with those packages of goods which they had been able to recover after pursuing them downstream.

Sitting disconsolately on the side of the boat, one of the boys remarked that though the seed corn had been saved, it was thoroughly wet and would doubtless mold before they could reach Sauquoit Creek and get it planted. He added, "I think we had better go back to Connecticut. It's the hand of God."

White, a sanctimonious man, declared that the hand of God was in it, and the hand was pointing, not backward toward Connecticut, but toward a partly overgrown river flat opposite, on the north bank. For the moment they would leave the cart in the boghole, unhitch the oxen, swim them across, then ferry the contents of the cart over to the field, plough and harrow the soil, and plant the corn. After the corn had ripened they would return in their bateaux and transport it to Sauquoit Creek. The boys blinked at each other, shrugged, then considered their father's suggestion.

Finally the youngest, the one who had been for returning to Connecticut, spoke up. "But Pa, after we get settled on the Patent—and that's farther up the river—and we get our potash made and our corn raised, how can we get it to market on a river that acts like this one?"

Instead of replying, White sat staring at the ground and shaking his head. Finally, he said slowly, "I doubt if anyone can answer that question. The flats in this valley will never be worth much until it is answered. Someday they may build a decent road. I wish I'd bought a farm along the Hudson but it's too late now. Well, let's go across and plough that field."

Remembering the stony clay of Connecticut, they marveled at the deep, loamy soil. On the second day they finished and pushed on upstream. By perseverance they arrived at the Patent on the appointed day. To White's great satisfaction he was fortunate enough to draw the first choice of land—the tract bordering the old military road and the west bank of Sauquoit Creek. Zephaniah Platt, the second partner, chose the flats between the road and the Mohawk River.

When the drawing was finished, Zephaniah Platt turned to his fifteen-year-old son, Jonas. "There's your inheritance, Jonas my boy; it's yours when you come of age and I think it's about all you'll ever get. However, it's good rich soil and the spring freshets will always keep it so."

After shaking hands with the other partners, Zephaniah and Jonas mounted their horses and rode eastward on the river road some fifty miles bearing north four miles at Caughnawaga to the seat of Montgomery County at Johnstown. There Zephaniah registered the boundaries of his tract and received his deed. Observing a wistful look in his son's eyes as he pocketed the document, Zephaniah asked him the reason.

Jonas answered quickly, "If some day I'm going to own land in this beautiful valley I think I'd like to do what that man does—I'd like to be the Clerk of this county some day."

Zephaniah patted his son's shoulder. "No reason why you can't, my boy. Just apply yourself to your studies and keep your aim in mind."

The more Jonas thought of this, as they rode by easy stages back to their home in Poughkeepsie, the stronger the desire grew. It was glowing in his heart like an opal three weeks later when he was helping to load the family's baggage into Conestoga wagons which the family servants would drive northward on the Claverack Road toward the Greenbush Ferry and Albany, whence they would rumble on to Glens Falls, Lake George, and Lake Champlain. Of course, Jonas had known of the imminent family departure and the reason. He had braced himself to parting with his Poughkeepsie friends, including Helen Livingston, perhaps forever. Still, in Montreal there would be other boys—and girls. But there would not be another Mohawk Valley. His valley. Or at least part of it was. As for the reason—his father was about to leave his home in Poughkeepsie to establish a new home on a land grant bordering Valcour Bay on Lake Champlain. His purpose was to set up a line of transportation between Albany and Montreal, partly by wagon but mostly by sloop and bateau. Zephaniah had faith in the future of commercial transportation.

Prior to the war he had become wealthy forwarding freight between Albany and New York in his own fleet of sloops. His appraisal of postwar freight movement had rated the Champlain route between the Hudson and the St. Lawrence as being the safest and the most dependable for international trade. In the event of blockades or embargoes of American ports that would be the only possible route for intercontinental freight. Certainly, the prospect of ocean transportation from New York to Montreal depended entirely on the dove of peace. There seemed to be no closed season on doves. Even in peacetime Atlantic coast-wise shipping suffered from the depradations of privateers.

By the end of summer Zephaniah, aided by his four sons and by his servants, had cleared enough land on both sides of the Saranac River at its confluence and had erected enough log cabins to create the appearance of a settlement. Scores of people came from Long Island to buy the fertile acres which Zephaniah was having surveyed. Jonas protested that amid such a multiplicity of business affairs his father would need his help. Nevertheless, the first boat leaving the rivermouth harbor that fall carried Jonas toward Montreal and a school noted for its discipline and scholastics.

* * * * *

During the next three years Jonas acquired not only the habit of study but a wish for a course in law. Accordingly, when he was eighteen his father sent him to New York City to study law in the office of Richard Varick. Varick had been for many years Mayor of New York.

From his desk in Varick's office Jonas, grown slender and handsome, saw most of the leading politicans in New York coming in to consult Mayor Varick. Through Varick, Jonas came to know them, their grudges, and their enemies. With a few exceptions they had one common characteristic. They often deplored a prevalent lack of loyalty, but they did not seem to know much about loyalty itself. Their imbalance of bitterness caused Jonas to wonder if there might be room in politics for sincerity and warm friendship. In other words, why could not some of them be more like a certain dignified young Poughkeepsie lawyer of his acquaintance named James Kent.

In the spring of 1788, Jonas' curiosity about the one-sidedness of politicians prompted him to take a brief holiday and attend the State Convention at Poughkeepsie on June 17.

* * * * *

The purpose of the Convention was to consider a Federal Constitution not yet ratified by all the Colonies. The Convention was held in the town hall but informal "back stage" discussions took place at a tavern down the street, where excellent draft beer was served in pewter mugs. Indeed the brew was so agreeably mellow and bitter that the question of whether New York should follow the example of the four states which had already adopted the Constitution, plus the three others about to do so, might have been decided in three or four days instead of dragging on until July 11. On that day a bulletin appeared on the tavern wall that there was no more beer. Therefore coffee only would henceforth be served. Strangely enough, the Convention promptly voted to accept the Constitution—providing that future amendments might be added.

* * * * *

It had been on Saturday morning of the first week of the meeting that James Kent, a twenty-five-year-old, bulldog-faced Yale graduate, and now a Poughkeepsie lawyer, ruefully closed his office door. For four days not a single client had lifted its knocker. His melancholy-appearing clerk, Smith Thompson, a Princeton alumnus and a lawyer who served Kent without pay, supporting himself by teaching school, accompanied Kent down the shady street to the tavern. The loud babble of voices from the taproom, audible as far as Kent's office, had roused their curiosity.

The taproom was a dirty, noisy place, smelling of tobacco smoke, beer and spirits. From the doorway it appeared that every bench at every table was occupied. The customers were leaning forward wagging a finger or pounding their mugs to gain the attention of their tablemates. Some were smiling, others scowling, but everyone was talking—no one listening. The harried tavern-keeper in a soiled white apron, with an arm full of foaming mugs clasped against a rotund belly built to support them, squeezed his way between the crowded benches. With one hand he served beer while the fingers of the other were busy acknowledging orders.

After a second look around, Thompson turned his sallow face and shouted in Kent's ear that he could see two possible places at a table near the center of the room. Kent nodded to him to lead the way. Before they had reached the table, one of its circle, a corpulent, jovial man with an aristocratic bearing and the florid cheeks and nose of an English country squire hailed Kent heartily as "Judge" and invited him to sit down. At the same time he shouted to the tavern-keeper with two of his fingers upright.

Kent extended his arm to grasp the hand of his hospitable friend greeting him genially with a "Hail, Gouverneur Morris, you old tub."

Morris' spreading waistline was wedged so tightly between two slender young men that in attempting to rise he partially lifted them from the bench. While shaking Kent's hand Morris jerked his head to the left, saying in a patrician drawl, "Meet Ambrose Spencer, Columbia County Clerk," and then to the right to introduce, "Young De Witt Clinton, Governor George's nephew. Boys, this is James Kent, smartest lawyer in the state."

Spencer and Clinton acknowledged the introduction with disdainful nods and the cool reply, "We've heard of Kent." Morris gave them a pained look, then sat down so suddenly that Spencer and Clinton lost dignity in trying to regain some portion of the bench.

From a corner of his eye Kent observed that his lank-haired assistant was giving all of his attention to another member of the circle who had been ignored during the introductions. He was a large, formidable man in a frilled snowy shirt, white waistcoat, and expensive black suit. Thompson's expression was that of a timid, impecunious young man admiring an overpowering, self-made man who had attained wealth with maturity. His loud forceful voice boomed, "Hello, Thompson. I was sitting at this table before your friends arrived. Since I've not had the pleasure of making their acquaintance perhaps you could do me the honor of introducing me to Mr. Morris and these other gentlemen."

With arching eyebrows Smith Thompson looked eagerly at his mentor, Kent, received an affirmative nod, then turned to the self-made man.

"Certainly, sir. Mr. John Tayler may I present Mr. Gouverneur Morris, one-time delegate to the Provincial Congress, Ambassador to France, leading member of the committee which drafted the Constitution, and a United States Senator. Gentlemen, Mr. John Tayler, one of our wealthiest men. He began his career as a mere Indian trader."

Tayler flushed slightly and gave Thompson a questioning

look, as Morris, in an effort to shake Tayler's hand, upset Clinton's mug. "Mr. Tayler. Indeed, sir. I had no idea. It is a pleasure," he said, adding derisively, "to meet so distinguished an Indian trader."

Instantly there was a hush which spread to the two adjoining tables. As the venom of Morris' cutting remark about "an Indian trader" sank in, a deep color suffused the harsh lines in Tayler's face. His hazel eyes grew round and hard. Morris hastily withdrew his hand masking his retreat with a succession of short mocking laughs. No one joined him. Tayler started to speak, then changed his mind. But his glare said plainly that in the future he would watch for a chance to even the score with Morris. And there would be no compromise.

Kent eased the tension by motioning to Thompson to sit down, then seated himself. The bench was so low and Kent was so short that his bull-dog face appeared just above the edge of the table. His grave expression, dark complexion, and rolling eyes heightened the illusion of a bull-dog. Then Kent waggishly cocked his head at Morris. Spencer and Clinton burst out laughing. From the corners of his eyes Morris gave them a pitying, almost contemptuous glance and stopped laughing. Smith Thompson looked from one to another in perplexity. Tayler's high cheeks wrinkled in a frosty smile which might have developed into a sympathetic laugh if a dish-faced woman in a Shaker bonnet had not placed her hand on the top of his head to lift herself through the narrow opening between Tayler's back and the back of the man behind him at the next table. She seemed to be trying to reach James Kent. When she finally got close enough to Kent to bend over him, he rolled his eyes up at her, raised two fingers and murmured "Two beers."

Instead of executing his order the woman thrust a quill pen between Kent's two fingers and shoved a paper under his nose. Kent scowled at it and said "What's that?"

The woman said sharply, "Read it, I want all of you to sign it."

As Kent hastily read the paper, color spread from his swarthy neck up through his face. Forcing the pen and paper back into her unwilling hands, Kent said in a voice which increased in volume and range until it had wrought a general silence in the taproom.

"Madam, I refuse to sign a temperance pledge. I have never been drunk and by the blessing of God I hope I never shall be drunk. However, I have a constitutional privilege to get drunk. I refuse to sign that privilege away."

The shirt-sleeved, white-aproned innkeeper set down two handfuls of foaming mugs, grabbed a twig broom and lunged at the woman shouting "Get out of here! You're spoiling my business!"

The woman eluded the first swing of his broom. At the doorstep he made a last ineffectual swing at her swirling petticoats and howled "Git!"

As the ensuing roar of laughter subsided, Morris applauded by pounding the table with his mug, shouting in his resonant, cultivated voice "Well done, Kent. As yet your constitutional privilege is a mere figure of speech, but it shows where you stand on the matter."

Kent arose, lifted in acknowledgment the nearest mug (Tayler's) and said "Gouverneur Morris, as a fellow Federalist, I propose a toast to the success of our attempts to establish a Federal Union."

Responding to the toast, Tayler was on his feet while Morris was still trying to extricate his girth from between the wedging Spencer and Clinton. Tayler reached for his mug, but Kent had taken it. Tayler shouted at the sweating tavern-keeper, "Hey! What's the matter with you? We're trying to drink a toast to the Constitution and I haven't any beer."

When the deficiency had been supplied, the toast was drunk. Tayler ostentatiously paid the score for everyone at the table. Morris watched Tayler's gesture with a derisive little smile, then keeping an eye on young De Witt Clinton, spoke casually to Kent, "Of course, Kent, you know why we are here. That charlatan Governor, George Clinton, this young gentleman's uncle, voiced his hope before the Legislature last January that nine states would unite in a Federal Union, and that New York, the strongest and most strategically located, would remain aloof. You know what that would mean, Kent. Two countries, the Federal Union divided geographically in two parts by New York State. George Clinton would become New York's dictator in effect, if not in name. And we, having fought perilously for eight years to escape becoming the subjects of King George, would find ourselves the slaves of Uncle George."

With an oath De Witt Clinton sprang to his feet and swung at Morris. With an agility remarkable in so stout a man, Morris avoided the blow. Instantly, Spencer pounced on Clinton and forced him down on the bench.

Morris shrugged and said calmly, "Our young friend De Witt seems excitable. He has taken my remark about his Uncle George as an insult, yet I don't think he's as devoted to his uncle as he would have us believe." Then, in an admonishing tone he turned to face De Witt. "As for you, young man, unless you are an extremely good pistol shot and experienced in duelling, I suggest that you remain seated."

Flushed and shamefaced, Clinton did not look up. After a pause he mumbled, "Sorry sir, I owe you an apology."

Morris spoke kindly. "Son, it's not my purpose to defame your uncle. As the first American Governor of New York, he guided us successfully though the war. History may mark him as one of our greatest. George Clinton was not to be the object of my remarks. When you interrupted, I was about to say that a house divided, soon falls. Therefore it is advisable that New York adopt the Constitution and become a member of the Federal Union. The alternative may lead us into civil war!"

James Kent interrupted. "Mr. Morris, I am in complete agreement. If there is the slightest chance of a civil war—should we fail to join our sister States—then in the face of every argument to the contrary, let us adopt the Constitution."

At this point a messenger arrived with the announcement that Mr. Melancthon Smith and Mr. Alexander Hamilton were about to resume their debate on the Constitution in the town hall.

* * * * *

Half an hour later, Jonas Platt, having ridden from New York in less than a day and a half, dismounted and tied his horse at a rack near the town hall in Poughkeepsie. At the open, double doorways he paused listening to the hortatory salvos from the speaker's platform. Perceiving in the back row of benches the well-remembered profile of James Kent, and a significantly vacant seat beside him, Jonas' face brightened. To reach that vacant seat Jonas had to climb over several pairs of feet, including those of Smith Thompson sitting next to John Tayler. Jonas gave them each a faint smile to compensate for stepping on their corns (Thompson and Tayler excepted) and sat down contentedly beside Kent.

Despite the frenetic key of the endless oratory which at one time touched on war, most of the audience was sleeping soundly. Decisions having already been made in private conferences, there was no necessity for staying awake. It was a hot day. Jonas' resolution to learn something was undermined by the snores around him. He observed that Kent was not only awake but alert and seemingly in the grip of some strong emotion. Indeed, he appeared hardly aware of Jonas' presence. In late afternoon the meeting broke up. Kent turned to Jonas with a warm smile, shook hands, and hospitably invited him to his home for tea.

In Kent's cottage, over steaming Bohea, Jonas said, "Mr. Kent, when the speaker addressing the convention said that failure to adopt the Constitution might lead to civil war, your face became set and white. The skin over your knuckles was tight. Do you really think that we might come to war?"

Kent's eyes flashed. "I hope not. I hate war. I saw a bit of it once."

Merry-eyed, nineteen-year-old Elizabeth Bailey Kent, a native of Kinderhook, New York, who was serving the tea urged him on. "Tell him, James. It's your most amusing story."

Kent, flushing, gave his wife a dour look, at which she slipped another lump of sugar into his cup. "To sweeten you, my dear. Now please tell Mr. Platt your story, and while you do so, you will please excuse me—I'm expecting a caller."

Kent glanced at the expectant Jonas. "Well, if you really want to hear it. In the summer of 1777, when I was fourteen, my parents were living at Danbury, Connecticut. British Army Headquarters had sent out a small detachment of men with a light fieldpiece on some sort of an alert. They landed at Saugatuck and marched up the Green Farms Road.

"Anticipating the raid, the local militia had rallied and barricaded that particular road just above the schoolhouse where I should have been in attendance. Instead, I was on the roof, hiding behind the chimney, hoping to see the sport unobserved. At a little distance the British halted and fired a cannon ball at the barricade. At least, I thought that was where they were aiming, but when the ball struck the chimney two feet above my head I was convinced that they had seen me and that I was the target. Among flying bricks

I hit the ground running. I headed for home and I doubt that a second cannon ball could have overtaken me!

"Ever since that fright in my youth I've had a mounting conviction that all war, and even preparation for war, is a senseless performance."

Jonas nodded, "I'm in complete agreement with you, Mr. Kent." He was about to add something further when they heard a chatter of feminine voices outside.

Mrs. Kent entered with a pretty girl whom she introduced as Helen Livingston, grandniece of Chancellor Livingston. Jonas struggled vainly to recall his thought, but he was lost in wonderment at why Helen Livingston whom he had loved all his life, but from afar, had to be introduced. But she did and although coolly courteous, she maintained the attitude of never having seen him before. As indeed she had not—not this Jonas.

After a supper flavored by clever small talk, James Kent asked Jonas if he had some particular ambition. Jonas replied quite simply that he hoped someday to become the Clerk of Montgomery County, explaining that the day he was admitted to the New York bar he would become the owner of a fine tract of land in Whitestown. From the corner of his eye he saw Mrs. Kent glance significantly at Helen, as if to say, "Your family could help him get that appointment." He knew that the Livingston family together with the Schuylers were leaders of the Federalist party in the State. Blushing, he wished that Mrs. Kent had not given Helen that look. He wanted to win that clerkship by his own efforts. And he was about to say so when Helen gave him a look that made him forget everything—but Helen.

CHAPTER TWO

JONAS PLATT

By July 12, when Jonas returned to New York, he had learned that Helen Livingston could make him feel like a small boy, although she was but three years his senior, and that she was willing to become Mrs. Platt, but not if she would have to live in Whitestown. At first dismayed by her objection, Jonas had countered with a glowing description of the charms of the upper Mohawk.

Helen had admitted that it might look that way to anyone riding through on horseback, but as for the realities of Whitestown—well, she had met a woman who lived there, a Mrs. Amos Wetmore.

Whitestown,* according to Mrs. Wetmore's nasal complaining opinion, was a town without streets, houses, stores, or even a town hall where dances and sewing circles could be held. It was indeed a mere scattering of pioneer farms and log cabins recently hacked out of the wilderness. There was no store nearer than the ruins of old Fort Schuyler some six miles down-river, and that was only a trading post. Three miles up-river there was a village of Oneida Indians led by Saucy Nick who stole every chicken and cow which strayed near the woods. And nowhere were the woods far away!

During the summer everyone slaved from dawn until dark. In winter it was a question of survival. For a courthouse the men used a barn. Court met on the rare occasions

*Whitesboro, New York.

when someone was lucky enough to acquire (no one asked how) a keg of gin.

There was a dilapidated log structure with four small windows (two with broken panes) known as the Presbyterian Church where the Reverend Bethuel Dodd held Sunday services in any sort of weather. The few moments following Divine Services were the only opportunities the women of Whitestown had of forgathering for gossip. Men could scarcely understand the craving of women for those strictly feminine meetings where they all talk at once. And even after women had started for church they could not be sure that they would attend.

On a pleasant Sunday morning in early autumn, Mrs. Wetmore had managed to convince Mr. Wetmore that she did not need any more brook trout but that she did need spiritual guidance. The bitter argument had lasted so long that they were late in starting for church. No one was in sight as they walked along the road. Mr. Wetmore's thoughts were not on God. He was looking for a bee tree which someone had recently told him about. Not two hundred yards from the church he had spied the tree. High up in the branches he had also spied a black bear.

The bees had pretty well convinced the bear that the honey was not worth it. Indeed, he had already started down. Mr. Wetmore shouted at the bear. The bear looked down at him, then up at the bees, and stayed put. With terse emphasis Mr. Wetmore informed Mrs. Wetmore that there was a month's supply of meat up in that tree and he expected her to stand there while he ran to the nearest neighbor to borrow a musket and ammunition. It would be her further duty to shout and clap her hands if the bear started down. If that failed to keep him up there, she could try throwing stones at him.

Mrs. Wetmore expostulated that devotion to God was more important than shooting a bear. Mr. Wetmore told her not to be a fool. If they should go to church, they could do no more than pray for meat. And up in that tree was the answer to the prayer that they would pray. So why not shoot the bear and do the praying afterward?

Without listening to her further protests, Mr. Wetmore bustled off.

Mrs. Wetmore stood cold with fear, yet inwardly seething. From the distant church she heard faintly the whine of the congregation singing hymns. Just then the bees swarmed on the bear's nose. The bear started down. Mrs. Wetmore wanted to run, but nightmarish fear had paralyzed her. At that moment her husband returned with a musket. Sharply ordering her to stand still, he rested the heavy gun on her shoulder and shot the bear dead.

With a complimentary remark about the gun Mr. Wetmore hurried away to return it. He went on to his house, fetched his ox-team and stone-boat and rolled the bear on it. About that time the church service had ended, the congregation, straggling up the road, had overtaken the Wetmores. They had grouped themselves around the stone-boat and, like a self-appointed guard, accompanied the Wetmores all the way home. Not a word of rebuke or reproach had been spoken, but their silence had been even harder to endure. Wetmore hung the carcass in the enclosure behind the house, cut and quartered it, and passed the meat to his wife. She dried it over an open fire, since it must firm before she could cut it up and render the fat. Meanwhile, Wetmore had stretched the pelt on the barn door, scraped it clean, and left it to dry. By the time winter had come the indignation of the less pious had moderated to a degree which permitted them to try to borrow the bearskin rug.

And that, Helen said, was why she was unwilling to live in Whitestown.

At the conclusion of her repetition of Mrs. Wetmore's story, the indignation in Helen's voice had mounted to such a pitch that Jonas resolved to say no more to her about Whitestown.

However, he was not to be diverted from his original intention. He asked Mayor Varick what procedure to follow to become eligible as a county clerk.

The mayor explained that in New York State the authority to make all civil appointments was conferred upon a Council of Appointment comprising four State Senators, one from each of the four State Senatorial districts. The members of this Council were elected by the Assembly. It consisted at this time of two Federalists, Philip Schuyler and Philip Livingston and two anti-Federalists, Mr. Savage and Mr. Cantine. Within the Council a vote was taken on each contemplated appointment. In the event of a tie, the Governor cast the deciding vote.

Mr. Varick explained further that because the voters of the upper Mohawk Valley were a restless, unpredictable people and strongly anti-Federalist, the Federalist leaders had asked Mr. Schuyler and Mr. Livingston to appoint a Federalist clerk for Montgomery County to give their party something of a foothold there. Also, although Governor Clinton as an anti-Federalist could, by his deciding vote, prevent such an appointment, he was, nevertheless, willing to concede that point in exchange for another political advantage.

For several months both Schuyler and Livingston had been considering the value of negotiating with Savage and Cantine for the clerkship of Montgomery County with a view to offering it to Jonas as soon as he had passed his bar examinations and become of age. Their preference for Jonas was partly because of their liking for his father, and partly because Jonas had always been courteous and reserved when they met him in Mr. Varick's office.

Varick reminded Jonas that the bar examinations were only some twenty months hence and that he must decide whether or not he would make his permanent residence in Montgomery County. He added that a frontier residence would be neither comfortable nor entirely safe.

For a year and a half, Jonas wrestled with the problem of living alone in Whitestown with its prospect of growth and expansion, or in probable obscurity in a more civilized community with Helen. Eventually, he told Mr. Varick that he would accept the clerkship *if* he could get it. He put off telling Helen because he was afraid that she might break the engagement. He would tell her after the wedding. Meanwhile, he deluded himself with the hope that if he *should* be appointed, she might possibly change her mind. But should the appointment be offered him before they were married, he would accept it and abide the consequences.

Within hours after Jonas had told Mayor Varick of his resolution, Helen knew about it. Because Jonas had not told her she was furious, but when she received the secret information that Jonas' application had been ignored, an outraged sense of justice made her even more furious. By clever manipulations among the Livingstons and by exerting a considerable influence among the wives of the Schuylers, whom she knew intimately, she was able to effect a reversal of the decision and obtain for Jonas the appointment. It came late in 1790 after their marriage. Without confessing her efforts on his behalf, Helen agreed to "try living in Whitestown," but it was May of the following year before they arrived. By that time Whitestown was in the newly created county of Herkimer and Jonas was its first clerk.

Jonas and his wife put up at a log farmhouse. The next day he looked about for a man to help him dig a cellar and erect a house, barn, and office. But it seemed that nearly every landowner in the entire Whitestown district was also trying to hire help. Jonas was despairing when a lanky, dejected Negro appeared and introduced himself as Dempsey

Slater. He confessed that he was a freed slave and produced a certificate to prove it. He had bought a small piece of land with a cabin on it in the town of Deerfield and had the receipt for the purchase with him, but because he had been a slave he had been refused a deed.

Jonas promised a resurvey of the land and a deed showing clear title. "But before I can do this," Jonas told him, "I must build my house and office. If you will bear a hand at the prevailing wage, I'll agree to make your survey my first act as County Clerk."

Slater accepted at once and went to work. He proved to be a skilled carpenter. Excavation and construction proceeded so satisfactorily that Mrs. Platt began unpacking her household goods.

When the cellar had been dug and walled with logs and the studs were up, a formidable looking Indian came idling by to speak with his friend Slater. Slater introduced him as "Saucy Nick." Jonas offered to give the Indian a job, but Nick refused, quite content to squat, smoke his pipe, and watch Jonas and Slater work. When he noticed Mrs. Platt unpacking a pair of balance scales, he became interested, muttered something under his breath and left.

The next day he returned with a huge yellow pike he had just caught and asked Jonas if he wanted to buy it at five cents a pound. Jonas was pleased to have it though it weighed fourteen pounds. Slater, who stood by while it was being weighed cast a doubting glance at Nick, borrowed a knife from Jonas, and slit the pike open. Out dropped several pounds of pebbles that Nick had crammed down its gullet. Instead of showing resentment, Jonas laughed at the attempted deception, then paid Nick (for pebbles as well as fish) seventy cents and gave him the knife as well, and some fishhooks, line, and tobacco. After the pike was cooked, he shared that too, with Nick.

Nick became suspicious and departed, never having been

treated so generously by a white man. However, when he returned, several days later, he had with him a band of young Oneidas. They saw Jonas and Slater struggling to raise the rooftree of a second building and sprang to help them. The heavy timbers were soon in place and, as though to celebrate, they danced on the rooftree for Jonas and his wife to the rhythm of a small drum which they carried.

As soon as the last cabin was completed, including the glass for its windows, and its furnishings had been installed, Jonas put up a post in front of it with a swing sign, on which he had painted the legend, "Office of Clerk–Herkimer County. Attorney-at-law. Jonas Platt." Then he sat down at his desk to await the coming of clients. He wondered if he should clear a path through the brush between the road and his door, but that proved unnecessary for his clients soon beat the path. It seemed to Jonas that every land title in Herkimer County must be imperfect. In two weeks, enough legal work had accumulated to tax his energies for two months.

He received as fees jugs of whiskey, sacks of grain, kegs of honey, barrels of potash, pelts, and even sawed lumber. Jonas soon found it necessary to have Slater build a warehouse in which to store this strange assortment of "fees." This was no more than finished when it became necessary to put up another.

Jonas enquired carefully into freight rates, both by bateau and by wagon to Schenectady and Albany, and soon learned that the cost of transporting such goods as he was storing almost equalled their sales prices in the Albany market. The only profitable commodities were living creatures such as pigs, sheep, cattle, and horses—they could walk to market. Unfortunately, livestock was not plentiful on the frontier. Under these conditions, thought Jonas, "There's little likelihood of prosperous communities being founded to the west of us. Whitestown will continue as a poor frontier settlement until something is done to provide cheap transportation."

Meanwhile, isolation was breeding in the frontier people such concern over their land boundaries and riparian rights that ill feeling developed among them which often blossomed into feuds. They shot, trapped, and snared all the game they could, dug edible roots, picked berries, gathered and dried medicinal herbs, caught fish, and clubbed wild pigeons from their roosts on their neighbors' property. At the same time they tried to keep neighbors off their own land.

Their staple diet was the corn and wheat they raised, but they had difficulty in getting it ground. Mill sites were numerous, but the building and maintaining of a mill dam, the procuring of the millstones, nearly all of which were imported from abroad and the building of the mill itself, exceeded the means of all but a few. Consequently, when a settler wanted some grain milled, he often had to carry it on his back a long distance, sometimes ten or twenty miles. Since oxen were superior to horses as draft animals, horses were scarce. But the oxen were so slow that the settlers preferred to carry the grain, even though it weighed a hundred pounds or more.

There were sawmills too, though it was possible to saw logs into planks or boards with handsaws by rolling the logs over a pit. But it was a two-man job—one in the pit and one above the log. Hence the possession of a sawmill or gristmill gave its owner a political advantage over his customers. He could exact his own price (and the price might be a political vote), or could even refuse those who came, making it necessary for them to walk to a more distant mill.

Hugh White, founder of the community and owner of the riparian rights of both banks of Sauquoit Creek, was the only man rich enough to build a mill dam. On May 17, 1787, he made an agreement with two neighbors, Amos Wetmore and John Beardsley, whereby he was to build a dam and they were to build a sluice with its gate on White's property and a gristmill on Wetmore's farm. The agreement was carried out, and the following year a sawmill was added. Beardsley did the building. He and Wetmore each received a quarter interest while White took a half interest in the entire project.

As the stones rumbled in the mill grinding corn, and the long straight saw, with powerful steady strokes, ripped the logs into boards, White revealed his scheming nature. Because of some minor incident, he threatened to close the sluice gate, thus shutting down the mill.

When Wetmore slyly hinted it might be opened after dark, White swore that he would destroy the dam should they attempt it. White also insisted that he would be within his rights since the original agreement of 1787 was only verbal. However, he told them there was no need to get excited about it, but as a further agreement, Wetmore must build a dam at his own expense on his own property and divert half of the stream's flow onto a field bordering the stream which White had conveyed to his son. Also, Wetmore must agree to become a Presbyterian and join the congregation of the Reverend Bethuel Dodd!

Of course the case went to court. Due to White's influence, it dragged along several years until the Court of Errors, in 1805, rendered a decision in favor of Wetmore.

Hugh White, an eccentric and a village tyrant, was typical of the settler who invariably appeared in those isolated communities and by his wealth and arrogance, subjected his neighbors to his fanatical whimsies. When the Reverend Carnahan, who succeeded Dodd, asked for permission to pasture a cow in one of White's fields, the request was refused. White gave his tenants, and those buying land from him by deferred payments, the privilege of paying him in hours of labor instead of dollars which were scarce. It was his custom to supervise all work done for him, and because he disliked to walk he rode a poor gray pony which sagged in the middle. White weighed a full two hundred and fifty pounds.

Perhaps it was because White was an uneducated man that he longed for the manifestations of learning. Recognizing this, Jonas contrived through family influence to have White appointed as Judge of the County Court. To insure the dignity of this very important office, White leaned heavily on Jonas for direction in court matters. Thus the selfish and dictatorial White, once feared by some and hated by the entire community, became a puppet in Jonas' hands. But Jonas made no effort to reform him. He preferred White as he was, so that he could make use of him as an instrument for helping those who appealed for aid. It was White's real nature to spurn such people. Yet Jonas, by his influence over White, earned for the latter an undeserved reputation as a man rough in manner but kind of heart.

Toward the end of October, Jonas conceived a plan for furthering his political career. The idea was unique and untried, but because it was based on the reaction of the people of that area to the kindness he hoped to render them, he felt sure of success. Because his plan would necessitate his absence from home for weeks at a time, he suggested to Helen that she go to Poughkeepsie, where she could spend the winter in comfort and return in the spring. A Whitestown winter with its nightly serenade by screaming panthers and howling wolves might cause her to decide to return to Poughkeepsie in the spring and stay there.

At the mere mention of going home, Helen, like many young wives agreed with alacrity. She was obviously bored with Whitestown, and perhaps a little bored with him. Jonas rode with her as far as Albany where he placed her on a down-river sloop. Then, with a sweet feeling of freedom, he concentrated on his plan.

As a first step, Jonas bought a small chest, fitted it with

forceps for pulling teeth and cloves to ease the resulting pain; also, the simplest medicines for reducing fevers and other common ailments, although he knew only the rudiments of their uses. Then to satisfy a yearning which he knew he would find as he went from trapper's cabin to farm, he included a generous supply of cigars.

It was doubtful if Jonas suspected the motive which led the Negro, Slater and the Indian, Saucy Nick, to face with him the dangers and hardships of the sparsely settled white wilderness. It was not because he had befriended them but because they had seen his medicine chest and believed that he was risking his life to aid and comfort the sick.

They knew that during the winter months there was sickness wherever there were people. They had resolved to help Jonas' efforts at healing, each in his own way. Nick relied on herbs, poultices, and strange potions after the manner of his people, while Slater believed in the laying on of hands, reading from the Bible, and the efficacy of prayer. They said little, but in the hearts of each was born a determination to bring Jonas back, safe and sound. Indeed, it is doubtful if Jonas could have survived without their knowledge of woodcraft, their strength and devotion. Yet Jonas, unconscious of the safety that surrounded him, gave little thought to danger, but rather to the political gains that would accrue to him and to wishing most earnestly that he knew more about surveying.

Jonas hired Slater to build a toboggan and bought from Nick three pairs of snowshoes for the trip. Though the snow deepened in the forest, the three set out with the avowed purpose of visiting every voter in Herkimer County. Nick broke the trail. Jonas followed, pulling the toboggan, while Slater pushed from behind with a pair of handles he had rigged. Axe, ammunition, musket, blankets, food, and the medical chest were carried on the toboggan. In it, besides the medicines Jonas was to use, was a leather pouch belonging to Nick into which he had crammed many smaller pouches, each containing a different medicinal herb. Also included was a small wooden box which Slater brought along containing his Bible.

Jonas found cases of sickness wherever he went. When he had done what he could for the sick, the rest of the family would be eager for news. Above all, they wanted to know when the State would build a road into their neighborhood or, better still, a canal. Another topic that lingered on the tip of every tongue was, "How long would it take the Americans to clear the Indians out of that rich land north of the Ohio River?" They explained that they planned to relocate out there so that they could ship their goods across the Lake to Canada or down the St. Lawrence to Montreal. They had heard that Canadians were good customers and a friendly people with whom to do business.

This widespread reaction among the people living beyond the end of the road gave Jonas pause. The Canadians were indeed nice people. He had lived among them. But they had sworn allegiance to the British Crown. And the Crown was hostile to the United States. Though the torch, the musket, and the scalp yell had failed to conquer the Americans, the agreeable dealings of Canadian lake-schooner captains might succeed in converting some of them. Americans south of the Ohio River were willing to be quoted when admitting that they hated Congress.

If those people who would someday settle north of the Ohio River should prefer the Crown to Congress, the flag might follow trade. The American Revolution might have been won only to be lost because people could not get their goods to market.

To Jonas it may have seemed that the strangest thing of all was that no one in the Mohawk Valley was doing anything about it, and few were even saying anything about it.

CHAPTER THREE

THE LOCK NAVIGATION COMPANY

Actually, it was two nonresidents of the Mohawk Valley who, perceiving the dilemma of the settlers in central New York, took the initial steps of proposing certain solutions. Elkanah Watson, an impetuous, explosive man, the originator of state fairs, the man who first brought Merino sheep to this country and the founder of the American woolen industry, visited George Washington during the winter of 1785 for the purpose of consulting him on the subject of canals. Watson learned only that although Washington was interested in canals he did not know much about them.

In 1788, while attending the second Fort Stanwix Treaty, Watson, ever alert for a prospect of some general commercial improvement, conceived the idea that Wood Creek, a tributary of Oneida Lake, and the Mohawk River could be connected by a short ditch. Watson's idea of a canal was to clear the driftwood and obstructions from natural streams. For over a hundred years white men had used Wood Creek and the Mohawk River for transportation. Before that it had been an Indian trade route for several hundred years. But to Watson the idea was a unique and personal discovery.

The other man, General Philip Schuyler, while travelling in England in 1761, had carefully examined the dug canals of that country. It must have been apparent to him that because the water level in a dug canal could at all times be controlled, and because there was little or no current, it was the only successful type of canal. Unfortunately, Philip Schuyler, one of the greatest Americans, was an unassuming man and did not press his ideas. He inclined toward letting positive, peppery little men like Watson have their way.

Christopher Colles, an Irish immigrant of 1765, had first proposed inland navigation to the New York State Senate on November 3, 1784. At that time, the Senate, knowing that Colles was impecunious, and anticipating a touch, had rejected his petition so far as public expense was concerned. They might have considered giving him a franchise to form a company and execute the work at his own expense. In the supply bill of 1785 the State Assembly voted $125 to Colles to draw a plan for removing obstructions from the Mohawk River. Colles made the survey and published a pamphlet containing a plan of Mohawk River improvement at an estimated cost of £13,000. The legislators looked at this figure, glanced at Colles over their spectacles, and changed the topic of conversation.

The subject of inland navigation came up again in the State Legislature on March 17, 1785, but failed to receive serious consideration, due chiefly to the prevailing abhorrence toward spending money.

By March 24, 1791, the Legislature had recovered sufficiently to pass a resolution ordering "a survey of the land between the Mohawk River and Wood Creek at Fort Stanwix and an estimate to be made of the expense necessary to construct a canal sufficient to float loaded boats of a ton and a half burden, and to report to the Legislature." One hundred pounds were appropriated for the expense.

During the summer of 1791, Jonas Platt, as clerk of Herkimer County and as an interested citizen, eagerly awaited the arrival of the surveyors, Major A. Hardenburgh and Benjamin Wright. They came in September, rode on to Fort Stanwix, and ran a line suitable for a ditch between the Mohawk River and Wood Creek. They returned to

Albany and handed the State Treasurer £40 of the £100 allotted them for expenses. Hardly had they ridden out of Whitestown when Jonas was spreading the news that such was the integrity of the men who were promoting the canal. A few day later Jonas' claim was substantiated when four gentlemen from Albany passed through Whitestown in the Schenectady–Fort Stanwix stage. They were Elkanah Watson, General Van Cortlandt, Stephen Bayard, and Jeremiah Van Rensselaer. They were investigating possible improvements in the water route from Schenectady to Seneca Falls. They were all wealthy or influential and of excellent reputation.

Jonas did not learn the results of their investigation until some time afterward. Most men of that time revealed their thoughts or talked freely only when their emotions were aroused to the point of explosiveness. The rest of the time they were secretive. Consequently, the reports of current affairs were often fragmentary. One had to be patient to learn the whole story. It took Jonas nearly four years to piece together the history of the canal project in New York State, beginning with the memorable journey of Elkanah Watson and his associates on wilderness streams to Seneca Falls.

During the trip Watson had kept a journal in which he described the frequent short rapids in the Mohawk River, the portages, the driftwood in Wood Creek and its tortuous course, Lake Oneida, the Oneida and Seneca Rivers, and the probable expense of removing obstacles to navigation by bateau. He devoted a couple of pages to the salt springs at Onondaga Lake. He described them in part as follows: "Those [salt] works are in a rude unfinished state but are capable of making about 6,000 bushels of salt per annum which is nearly the quantity required for the present consumption of the country—When the mighty canals shall be formed and locks created it will add vastly to the facility of an extended diffusion and the increase of its intrinsic worth."

He added, "They could only transport from one and a half to two tons in a flat boat at an expense of from $75 to $100 a ton from Schenectady to this place [Rome, New York]." Watson might have added that the down-river freight rate, which would affect all of the trade goods produced on the frontier, was proportionately high—so high that the cost of transportation nearly equalled the market price of the goods. Whatever was produced on Whitestown frontier farms was also being produced in the Hudson Valley where water transportation to New York was available during most of the year. Consequently, Hudson Valley farmers prospered while those in the Mohawk Valley inclined to stagnate, especially at the frontier. Naturally, the Hudson Valley people were opposed to a canal through central New York State because it would greatly augment the volume of goods offered in the New York City market, increase competition, and depress prices.

Upon his return, Watson did not linger in Albany. He went on to New York where he gave the report and the journal of their westward trip to Philip Schuyler. The report and journal were molded by Schuyler into the pedestal of a canal act presented by Robert Williams in the Senate at the 1792 meeting of the State Legislature. Watson's companions in exploration backed the measure. Governor George Clinton spoke of the measure as "a useful improvement which could be made without the aid of taxes." The Governor's definition was a clear exposition of this early proposal. Its entire scope included only the clearing of the Mohawk River west of Schenectady and Wood Creek, plus a few locks which no one knew how to build so that they would be durable. Properly interpreted the Governor's words meant that that was about all they could get for nothing.

"Without the aid of taxes" was late eighteenth-century American "for nothing."

In a way it was unfortunate that the canal act was drafted by old-style Federalists. To minimize the expense of creating what they hoped would be a canal, they had fixed its western terminal not at Seneca Falls but at the mouth of Wood Creek at the eastern end of Oneida Lake. This terminal was approximately fifty miles east of the salt works at Onondaga Lake, one of the most important reasons for building the waterway. Sensing a sudden lapse in public enthusiasm for the project, Philip Schuyler had the act redrafted, shifting the western terminal to Seneca Lake and adding a northern lateral terminal on Lake Ontario at Oswego. The act, as it was finally submitted, included details of construction, permissible size of boats, and toll rates per ton. Fifteen years were allowed for completion of the work. The canal was to be built and owned by an incorporated company called the Western Inland Lock Navigation Company. The first question was "Who would be the Company?" The second was "How would the Company, after they knew whom they were, raise enough money to build the waterway?"

The obvious answer to both questions was that there must be a public sale of corporate stock. The subscribers would be the company. Purchasers of large numbers of shares would naturally be elected directors. The directors would elect officers.

According to the act of incorporation the stock subscription books of the Lock Navigation Company were opened concomitantly in the coffee houses of New York and Albany on the first Tuesday of May 1792. For three days a commissioner sat at a table in each city with an opened stock book before him, a cup of coffee, and doubtless a bottle of whiskey for lacing, but without enticing a single customer. Patrons of the coffee houses brought their friends to view the commissioners as if they had been monkeys in cages. Nearly everyone regarded them with sly amusement or open ridicule.

At the Tontine Coffee House in New York, Elkanah Watson watched anxiously from the background, like a playright at his first night when there are only a dozen people in the audience. Toward the close of the third day, Elkanah hurried forth to find at least one subscriber. He returned, followed by his brother James. James was literally dragging his feet. With drooping shoulders and an expression of resignation, James signed the book for twenty shares. Plunged in gloom, James sat down to a cup of coffee which Elkanah had generously provided. As he moodily sipped his coffee, James's face suddenly brightened with inspiration. There was really no reason why he should be the only sucker on the line. James scuttled out of the Tontine to return shortly with a string of enthusiastic friends who soon became stockholders.

This released Elkanah for a visit to the Lewis Old Tavern coffee house in Albany where the commissioner with his stock certificate book was regarded as a freak who could be seen without paying admission. Watson bought a few shares for himself, went out looking for customers, and returned with Philip Schuyler. Schuyler, who was regarded in Albany as a financial genius, bought ten shares. Shares sold rapidly thereafter.

In April of 1793 work was begun on the construction of locks at Little Falls. Because no engineer was available Philip Schuyler took charge of a force of some three hundred laborers. His chances of success would have improved if he had begun with a score of men. Having no one to advise them, Schuyler and the laborers had to learn everything connected with the hewing of canal locks through solid rock by experience. It might have taken a summer or two for Schuyler and a dozen men to discover the fundamentals of lock building. The following summer Schuyler could have appointed the dozen as bosses of the crew of three hundred and finished the work within the limit of the funds in the company treasury. Starting off with three hundred there was a lot of lost motion, men standing around awaiting orders, and a certain amount of confusion. Probably Schuyler foresaw all of this, but went ahead anyway because the shareholders, the prospective buyers of shares, and the Legislature were all looking for quick results.

The Lock Navigation Company's funds were soon exhausted and, due to a lack of response on the part of the public in buying further shares, the funds were insufficient to continue such a large payroll. Fear possessed the directors of the company. Apprehending an imminent shortage of funds, they resolved that the shareholders must be assessed. Little short of panic resulted. Those who had bought on deferred payments sacrificed their investment believing that their first loss would be their best loss and, since it had been a speculation, some penalty might well be expected.

With very limited funds some work was continued; Wood Creek was cleared and its course shortened seven miles by cutting across the loops and bends. By September some construction had been accomplished at Little Falls, but nothing had been finished. The funds of the Company had become exhausted. The entire project was abandoned for the time.

However, landowners in central New York, still hopeful of the completion of the work, bought more shares. Schuyler and his associates, fully convinced of the economic necessity of the canal, bought again. By early winter a sufficient sum had accumulated in the treasury to permit Schuyler to resume construction. When the bitter January wind blew snow whirls from thick ice floes stranded on the rock ledges of Little Falls gorge, lion-hearted Philip Schuyler returned to the building of the locks. In Schuyler's life, duty, especially patriotic duty, came first. Physical comfort and even personal safety were of small concern.

While Schuyler and his workers were drilling through ice and rock, the Legislature convened in the old State House in Albany. The first act of the Assembly was to elect as Speaker James Watson, the first man to buy shares in the Lock Navigation Company. Their second act was to elect four State Senators to become the new Council of Appointment. The function of the Council of Appointment was to appoint men to fill vacancies all the way from sheriffs and justices of the peace to the State Supreme Court bench. According to tradition the Governor was expected to make the nominations. Then the Council voted on each nomination.

In the previous gubernatorial election George Clinton had defeated on a technicality, John Jay, a Federalist. In retaliation the Federalists in the Legislature wanted Federalist Egbert Benson on the Supreme Court Bench so that they could control it. To block them, Governor Clinton refused to nominate Benson.

When word of Governor Clinton's refusal reached Schuyler, who was a member of the Council, he mounted his horse, rode to the State House, and nominated Benson himself. Then he rode back to Little Falls. Both ways Schuyler must have suffered severely from the cold. He acted in devotion to his party and the best interests of the State, never suspecting that he had established a precedent which would introduce to New York politics the disgraceful spoils system.

However, the Legislature was so impressed with Schuyler's courage and selflessness that they voted favorably on James Watson's proposal that the State Treasurer be directed to purchase two hundred shares of Lock Navigation Company stock.

Work continued on the Little Falls locks through the

summer with such gratifying progress that by mid-November the five locks, each with a drop of nine feet, were far enough along to permit the passage of boats.

Schuyler was aware that no locks could be permanent unless made of squared stone blocks fitted together with cement. Having no cement nor enough money to buy cement, he built the locks of heavy logs, squared, matched, and pegged together, but in a short time they rotted away.

Schuyler had given of his best, but he knew that his best was not good enough. People who had remained snugly at home while he was stamping his feet on the ice at Little Falls would criticize his poor effort—and in his opinion rightly. He urgently needed someone with proper skill and engineering experience. To that end he wrote Robert Morris at Philadelphia requesting the loan of William Weston, a canal engineer who had had very considerable experience in England:

"The directors of the inland navigation companies in this state labor under a very disagreeable dilemma. They have engaged a large number of men to begin operations on the 15th of next month (May 1795) and have not been able to procure any person of the least practicable experience to conduct their operations. This has induced me to take the temporary superintendence of the business until an adequate person can be found. May I entreat your interference on the occasion and your recommendations to the directors (of the Schuylkill and Susquehannah Canal Company) to permit Mr. Weston to repair to this place as early as possible to avoid the errors we shall in all probability commit."

Weston accepted the offer of employment and took charge at Little Falls. His first step was to rip out Schuyler's wooden locks and replace them with stone available in a quarry a mile and a half away. Yet due to the lack of an insoluble cement, some of Weston's work ultimately proved unsatisfactory.

Weston continued to direct the work on the canal until 1799. He then returned to England. Benjamin Wright became the engineer in charge. Combining the information he had picked up from Weston with some ideas of his own, Wright so improved the first six miles west of Wood Creek that the directors ordered him to continue his work westward to Oneida Lake. But again an impoverished treasury brought all work to a halt.

As the directors of the Lock Navigation Company faltered and fumbled, debates broke out in the Legislature about whether the improving of waterways was such a good thing after all.

If there had been any doubt in the minds of such men as Jonas Platt and Joseph Yates, a young Schenectady lawyer, that the influence of central New York should make itself felt in politics, this crisis in canal affairs resolved their hesitancy. Jonas was well known and well liked, not only in central New York but in the Hudson Valley as well. He ran for the Assembly in the fall of 1795, was elected, and took office when they convened in New York City in 1796. On the last day of the session, due largely to Jonas' efforts, the State loaned the Lock Navigation Company $37,500, taking a mortgage on the canal and locks at Little Falls.

While in New York, Jonas renewed his acquaintance with his old friend, Thomas Eddy, a young promoter and speculator whose friendship he had gained while studying law in Mayor Varick's office. Eddy, grown wealthy, was now a director of the Lock Navigation Company. Jonas, who had from the first believed that the canal should be extended to Seneca Lake, now urged his arguments on Eddy. The original plan of connecting an improved Mohawk River with Lake Ontario was obviously of limited commercial value and not to be compared with the commerce that would be obtained by tapping the Onondaga saltworks and the vast fertile lands which lay to the westward of Seneca Lake.

As for connecting with Lake Erie by way of Lake Ontario, those great lakes were often too rough for travel by small boats. Then there was the "carry" over thirty miles of steep, rough roads to reach Niagara and Lake Erie from the Lake Ontario level.

After a long discussion and replies to countless questions, Eddy was finally convinced. As a director of the company, he in turn persuaded his associates to order the exploration of the "inland" route leading to Seneca Lake. This resulted in a survey of the route in 1796, made by Weston, Eddy, and a group of surveyors. Their report was favorable. Although there were no funds available with which to undertake the work, it was the beginning of the idea of an interior, protected route.

CHAPTER FOUR

FALL OF THE FEDERALISTS

Whether a canal route passed through Lake Ontario or was laid cross-country through central New York, the terminus would have to be on the extreme eastern shore of Lake Erie—within the military zone controlled by British-held Fort Niagara. According to the boundaries established by the treaty which concluded the Revolution, the British flag was not supposed to fly anywhere in North America south of the Great Lakes. In 1794, contrary to the provisions of the treaty, British troops still occupied Detroit, Fort Niagara, and Fort Oswego.

The British explanation for retaining those strategic "posts" was that American merchants, particularly those in New York, owed British merchants large sums of money for goods purchased by the Americans prior to the Revolution.

During the war the British had occupied New York City and for military reasons had confiscated an amount of property superior in value to the collective debts of the American merchants. Therefore, the Americans considered that they did not owe the British anything, and if the British thought that they did, they could jolly well come over to the United States and prove their claims in an American court. The British reply to that cordial invitation was to the effect that they "were not born yesterday," and would continue to occupy the "posts" with their troops. Furthermore, they would permit no American boats to pass either Oswego or Niagara.

Of course, the Americans could travel back and forth on

land south of the occupied zones, but that would take them through wilderness inhabited by bands of roving, hostile Indians. A few Americans tried it, but were soon afterward listed in the "Missing Persons" column.

Although the United States and Britain were nominally at peace, Britain had never recognized America as a sovereign state. Therefore, the Canadian Government had no compunction about freely supplying the Indians with arms and ammunition and encouraging them to attack the Americans wherever they found them. However, following General Wayne's decisive victory over the Indians at the Battle of Fallen Timbers on the banks of the Maumee in the Ohio country, and the Treaty of Greenville in 1794, the entire northwest was opened to American settlement. This victory also gave the British reason for a "second look" because their failure to support the Indians at Fallen Timbers broke forever their hold upon them.

During the war between England and France which broke out in 1793, both countries used it as a pretext to seize American ships, confiscate cargoes, and impress American seamen. Foreign and domestic commerce, even American finances were imperiled. As a last resort Hamilton sent to London John Jay,* Chief Justice of the United States Supreme Court. Jay's instructions were to conclude a treaty on practically any terms which would win recognition of the United States as a sovereign state and some reasonable stability for American commerce.

After four months of negotiating, assisted by the impact of Wayne's victory, a treaty called the "Jay Treaty" was ratified. It won for America the evacuation in June 1796 of the posts on American soil held by the British, along with other important details, but did not forbid the capture and imprisonment of American seamen nor did it revoke the prewar debts of American merchants.

*John Jay was a Federalist.

It was difficult to explain the advantage of this treaty to the satifaction of the man in the street, especially one on the sidewalks of New York. Relations with Britain remained strained, despite the treaty.

Before Jay's return from England he had been elected Governor of New York State. He landed in New York July 2, 1794. By July 4 the terms of the treaty had been made public. Although his effort to have the British evacuate the illegally held forts south of the Canadian border was of great moment in American history, the impatient hoi poloi in New York condemned his achievement because the evacuation date was set for 1796. He was severely denounced. With orthodox Independence Day spirit, the citizens of New York held a huge mass meeting that night and hanged and burned Jay in effigy, together with a copy of his treaty. This was enough to give pause to a man who had just saved his country and expected praise, not curses. While the treaty burned and the crowd howled, Alexander Hamilton, also a Federalist, stood on a porch shouting a speech in defense of the treaty. In the midst of his speech he was showered with half-bricks. While Chancellor Robert Livingston was feeding a copy of the treaty to the flames, his cousin Brockholst Livingston, a social lion, made a bulls-eye on Hamilton. That was the unkindest brick of all. The darkened porch door opened. Bleeding and inarticulate, Hamilton was dragged inside.

In January 1796, Governor Jay met with the Federalist-controlled Legislature in New York City. Among them was Jonas Platt, the newly elected Assemblyman from Herkimer County. Jonas had long been one of Jay's admirers and stood ready to support him with his vote, although he had never met him. The Governor's wife was a Livingston and therefore related to Jonas by marriage, though not closely enough to warrant an acquaintance.

Thomas Eddy was there, too. Jonas wanted very much to

introduce him to the Governor as another supporter of the development of waterways program. Eddy himself wanted to meet the Governor because the Lock Navigation Company needed a great deal more than the $37,500 appropriation previously made.

Jonas, attended by his faithful Negro servant Dempsey Slater, had taken rooms at the City Hotel for the duration of the session. Far into the night, lights blazed in the windows of the hotel. People plodding through the snowy streets looked up at them and wondered what new political plots were being hatched by those whose shadows moved so mysteriously across the frosted panes. Sleigh bells jingled as people arrived and departed. When the doors swung open, the buzz of conversation and the sound of laughter from within the lobby reached the street.

Late one evening, Slater, in a new woolen suit which he had made himself, stood in the lobby waiting for Jonas and watching the people who chatted as they milled about. He enjoyed the excitement, the fumes of cigars, the appetizing smell of freshly opened oysters, and the odor of liquors from the bar. Suddenly his attention was attracted by the entrance of an inconspicuous man with a sloping forehead, receding hair line, and scholarly manner. The man peered about anxiously. Slater eased over to him and asked if he could be of service. The man replied in a grateful tone that he was looking for General Philip Schuyler. Slater, who had been keeping track of the celebrities in the lobby by their loudly exchanged greetings, said that he would find General Schuyler. The scholarly man pressed a shilling into Slater's hand. Slater pressed it back, disappeared in the crowd, and returned with General Schuyler and Jonas Platt with whom the General had been talking.

General Schuyler's brow was puckered until Slater indicated the scholarly man. The pucker vanished in a warm smile as he greeted the man as "Governor Jay." General

Schuyler introduced Jonas. Jonas told Slater to find Mr. Eddy.

A few minutes later they were all sitting around the wood fire in Jonas' room while Slater concocted a hot spiced buttered rum. After sipping the rum, Governor Jay, glancing approvingly at Slater, asked for the recipe. Slater, smiling slyly, replied that he could not remember how he had made it. He had just made it. He added that whenever the Governor wanted a hot buttered rum he would come and make one, even though he had to travel a long way.

Visibly impressed by Slater's sincerity, Governor Jay asked Jonas if Slater was his slave. Jonas gestured to Slater to give the answer.

Looking squarely at Governor Jay, Slater said gently that he had been born a free man in Africa, made prisoner when his village was raided, and was sold into slavery. Transported to New York, he had been purchased by a Mohawk Valley farmer whom he had served faithfully for many years. When the farmer died he left a will granting Slater his freedom. Nevertheless, Slater had remained on the farm without pay serving the farmer's wife until her death two years later.

After a pause, the Governor asked Slater whether he bore white men any resentment. Slater shook his head and said that he liked white men and enjoyed making them happy and comfortable, asking in return only that they treat him with respect. Sometimes he accepted money for his services, and sometimes he did not. It really did not matter. What did matter was that nearly all of his people in America were slaves, and so long as they remained slaves they could not hope for respect. Indeed, they could hardly respect themselves. Like himself, many of the men of his race had each an attachment or feeling of devotion for some understanding white man like Mr. Platt, and the white man had responded to that devotion. But the Negroes under slavery were like children. Not until they were freed could they earn the white man's respect. Without respect they could not develop.

It might have been Governor Jay's memory of his bitter experience with the ungrateful mob some six months previously that caused him to become very thoughtful as Slater enlarged upon the basic need in every man for respect, and even for a little courtesy. Throughout, Slater's tones were forthright but not accusing. After he had finished speaking, they all sat in silence for nearly a minute. Then Governor Jay again looked squarely at Slater and thanked him for giving him something to think about.

Turning to General Schuyler, Governor Jay said that he had come to the hotel hoping to find the General. His purpose was to get a firsthand account of the waterways project.

In answering Governor Jay's questions, General Schuyler referred to Jonas for certain topographical information. Jonas, by deferring to Thomas Eddy, managed to include him in the conversation. Eddy, with frequent allusions to his personal investigation of the proposed waterway, summarized the situation convincingly.

Governor Jay again reflected, accepted another hot rum, and soon afterward departed remarking that it seemed to him that both the waterways project and the pratice of slavery deserved serious consideration by the public. They all arose as they bade the Governor good night. General Schuyler lingered, alternately gazing at the fire and at Slater. Finally, reaching some sort of conclusion, he wrapped his scarf about his neck, tapped Slater on the shoulder and said good night. Thomas Eddy shook hands with Slater and wished him good night. Left alone with Slater, Jonas told him that he was proud of him.

Slater's simplicity, kindliness, and faith had evidently spoken more loudly than his humble words.

A few days later, Governor Jay opened his beneficent

administration by persuading one of his friends to introduce a bill in the Assembly abolishing slavery in the State, giving the bill his entire influence and support. It failed of passage by a very close vote.

He was more successful in influencing the passage of an act providing for the loan of $250,000 to the Lock Navigation Company. As a consequence, by October 3 of the same year, 1796, a dug canal 1 3/4 miles long and large enough to accommodate boats of sixteen tons from the Mohawk River to the navigable portion of Wood Creek was completed. It was operated by the necessary locks and a feeder to augment the inadequate flow of the Creek itself. Soon afterward a channel 1 1/4 miles long, with a lock at each end, which cut off a bend of several miles, was also put into service at German Flats.

The men in New York City who once thought their Governor a fit target for rocks and ridicule now admitted him to be intelligent, wise, and forward looking, since he also recommended the improvement of highways, which resulted in the general highway act of 1797.

Turnpikes soon snaked westward from Albany. For the first several miles they were topped with fieldstone and bound with gravel and adequately crowned and ditched. But the more distant extensions were no more than recently cleared tracks through the forest. True, they crossed the lowlands and swamps on corduroy, but elsewhere they became deeply rutted, winding trails. Four and often eight horses were required to haul the heavy loads through the mire and up the steeper grades. But if these back-country turnpikes were not well maintained, the toll houses were. Rates were posted for vehicles and droves of cattle, sheep, and pigs. Each year, as the turnpikes crawled farther westward they tapped accumulations of grain, livestock, and other commodities, draining them eastward to the markets. Flocks of livestock were passed en route to Albany by the ever increasing number of westbound emigrants in their Conestoga wagons.

This pent-up commerce which Jonas had hoped would be released through the waterways was finding its outlet by way of the turnpikes as floodwaters find their channel. Yet he knew that the waterways must develop more slowly for they were far more expensive to build than the extensions of roads, which required little more than the hacking out of a track of uniform width through the forest. Great sums were obtainable only through the acts of the Legislature, and since the Federalists were, by and large, the "pro-canal" party, it was essential that they remain in power.

On March 15, 1798, Oneida County, which included Whitestown, was set off from Herkimer County, and Jonas was appointed its Clerk.

The creation of this county also created the 9th Congressional District of the State. As clerk, and as a Federalist in a county which had recently become Federalist in politics due to the influx of New Englanders, Jonas was the logical choice for Congressman at Washington. The following year he was elected to the House of Representatives in the Sixth Congress.

The Federalist party included American army officers who had survived the Revolution. Large landowners and the leaders of commerce and transportation were also Federalists. They were mostly men of British and Dutch descent, and somewhat inclined toward an aristocratic way of life. Such men as George Washington, Alexander Hamilton, John Jay, Philip Schuyler, and the Livingstons had brought the concept of a Federalist government through its embryonic state under the Articles of Confederation. They delivered the matured infant in 1789 when they elected Washington as President. The power of the States to govern themselves was made secondary to the authority of the national government as constituted in its executive, legislative, and judicial branches. They guided the struggling Republic through the 1790's from monetary chaos to sound money and national credit under the wise direction of Alexander Hamilton. These developments, seemingly impossible from the viewpoint of that time, had been achieved under the cloud of a threatened renewal of war with England.

Though the Federalists had proven themselves again and again capable of solving the difficult questions which had arisen, the year 1792 brought them face to face with an even more serious problem. The great French Revolution had broken out in 1789; the monarchy was overturned and a Republic (governed by the Directory) proclaimed in 1792. American sympathy was divided. There were those who sided with England as the upholder of law and order on the Continent while others, seeing in the French troubles a similarity to their own recently won freedom, sided with the Revolutionists. Political party lines were more sharply drawn; the Federalists were opposed to the Anti-Federalists, or as some called them, the Republicans.

The Republicans, the common people, "champions of the humbler classes" were headed by ex-Governor George Clinton and were openly sympathetic toward the French Revolutionists.

With so much political strife rampant in America, President John Adams, to forestall a similar Revolution in this country, pushed through Congress the "Alien and Sedition Acts." These acts provided that anyone guilty of circulating a petition voicing opposition to the "acts" might be arrested and tried in a Federal court.

Because of a fancied imminence of an uprising of the common people in the United States similar to the French Revolution, the Federalists believed their only remaining recourse to be the relentless enforcement of the Alien and Sedition Acts. Tragically for them, they seemed to forget Governor Jay's warning that they were still in power not because the electorate liked them, but because the voting majority had less liking for the new party—the Republicans.

The first attempt at enforcement began in poverty-stricken Otsego County. Hoping to earn the gratitude of his destitute neighbors, Jed Peck, an Otsego County judge, Republican, and member of the Legislature, offered a bill for abolition of imprisonment for contract debt. The Federalists in the Legislature, being of the lending class, scowled at Peck. In their opinion the type of man who could not repay money which he had borrowed belonged in jail. That was what jails were for. They considered that Jed Peck was wrong-headed to offer such a motion. They soon learned that he was even more dim-witted than they had suspected.

John Armstrong, carrier of a message from General Gates to General Arnold at the Battle of Saratoga and later the author of the Newburgh letters, wrote a petition against the Alien and Sedition Acts to be signed by the public. There was nothing in the Acts prohibiting the writing of a petition, but the circulating of that petition violated a provision. Armstong's interpretation of obeying the law was to leave a number of copies of the petition in a place where Jed Peck would be sure to find them. Peck did find them, and being a naive, obliging fellow, carried the petitions to the farms in Otsego County and left them to be signed, promising to return later and pick them up.

Hidebound, inflexible Judge Cooper, chancing upon some of the copies and noting the harsh language in which their message was expressed, demanded that U. S. District Attorney Harrison enforce the Alien and Sedition Laws. Mr. Harrison in turn demanded a bench warrant from a Federal grand jury for Peck's arrest. The warrant was issued. Peck was dragged from his bed at night, manacled, and forced to walk behind the tailboard of a cart to New York City, a distance of two hundred miles. By getting an early start each morning and walking right along, Peck reached New York in five days. It proved to be the funeral march of the Federalist Party. Everywhere along the way people came out in the road and asked questions. When they learned of the arrogance of Judge William Cooper they started a hue and cry against the whole Federalist Party.

At that time there was a normal number of conspiracies and incipient seditions to be found in New York State with a little seeking, but they received slight attention. Jed Peck, walking with bowed head at the tailboard of a cart, stole the show. He was hailed along the road as a martyr to free speech, free press and the right to petition. Small wonder that he bowed his head—he carried the wholehearted sympathy of the people and the press. He might reasonably have fallen on his knees and bawled in self-pity.

Armstrong, understanding Judge Cooper's impulsive zeal in meting out punishment, had timed his ruse to occur just before the spring election of 1800. The Jed Peck affair achieved such widespread publicity that the Republicans* swept the election all over the country.

The preceding December George Washington had died. Under the stars the banner of the Federalists lay broken across his grave, never again to be borne victoriously in national political campaigns. As the power of the Federalists ebbed all hope of success for the Lock Navigation Company sank with the declining influence of its supporters. The large landowners, shipowners, merchants, the bankers were "out." The artisans, mechanics, shopkeepers, and small farmers were "in." Wealth and enterprise in trade had fallen into disrepute. President John Adams was succeeded by Thomas Jefferson. Treacherous, volatile Aaron Burr, not tolerated by the Federalists, became the Vice-President. He was a frustrated and dangerous man and quite typical of a powerful element in the Republican party.

*The Republican party of that time has been regarded as the predecessor of the present Democratic party.

Jefferson, to forestall a further concentration of power in the national government, removed the Capital from Philadelphia to Washington, D. C. There the states' rights Faithful could keep an eye on it. The rest of the United States was now entirely at the mercy of the political types known as "Spell-binders" and "Friend of the People." No longer could a small group of conservative, wealthy men by mutual agreement and decision direct the policies and efforts of the masses. Further development of inland waterways would have to mark time until the general public could be educated to the military as well as economic necessity of the project and emotionally aroused into doing something about it. To get it out in front, the cause needed to be championed by a "Friend of the People."

CHAPTER FIVE

DE WITT CLINTON

In New York, De Witt Clinton, private secretary to his uncle, ex-Governor George Clinton, stepped forth in 1801 as a "Friend of the People." He had cuffed his way upward to become the political boss of New York City. He had orated himself into a seat in the State Senate and connived a membership in the Council of Appointment. He was thirty-two years old, a student of history and natural science, and an accomplished pistol duelist. Feared by his friends, agreeable when it was to his interest but normally grumpy, he was also fickle, selfish, arrogant, bold, and inclined to underrate the intelligence of his friends and opponents. Without motive he never tried to please anybody. Even his own confidential secretary Jabez Hammond hated him. If someone wished to please him there was only one sure way—to guarantee him a dozen or so votes.

Besides being a "Friend of the People," De Witt was backstage an even better friend of the Clinton family, including his in-laws such as Ambrose Spencer, who had married his wife's sister. But best of all, and nearest and dearest to De Witt's hard heart, was his lifelong intimate and grand passion—De Witt Clinton.

Clinton early achieved ascendancy over his friends and associates by becoming belligerent in his manner whenever they showed signs of disagreeing with him. If they persisted in disagreeing, he would raise his voice and glare. If that failed to impress them, he would insult and even threaten them.

Each member of the Council of Appointment had as much right to his choice of public officeholders as De Witt Clinton, but after a few collisions with De Witt they gave less thought to political appointments and more to escaping his public rebuke and abuse. The only way whereby they could make him smile was by agreeing with him, even when he contradicted himself. De Witt Clinton not only dominated the Council of Appointment he *was* the Council of Appointment.

To establish his power in the State, Clinton, as the self-appointed voice of the Council of Appointment, discharged from public office, regardless of proven ability, every Federalist but one. He replaced them with Republican politicians, not all of whom were able. This marked the beginning of the spoils system for which kind-hearted Schuyler had all unknowingly opened the door. Clinton, without scruple, was the first to walk through.

The one Federalist not immediately replaced was Josiah Hoffman, the State's Attorney General. Clinton knew that his brother-in-law, Ambrose Spencer, wanted that position, but was not quite ready to take it. Later, when Spencer was ready, Hoffman was turned loose like the others. In dealing out other public offices Clinton tried to bind the Clinton family into a loyal unit, believing that while blood is thicker than water, money is "thicker" than blood. Finding this belief operable, he extended its functioning to include the neglected Livingstons and some of the Schuylers.

Because of their numbers and influence the Livingstons and the Schuylers controlled an impressive number of votes. For them De Witt Clinton had not only appointments, but a sunny smile. His own relatives had to get along without the smile. Mrs. De Witt Clinton was a wealthy woman. She opened her purse to her husband, but not unless he included her in that smile. He was said to have been quite affable around the home.

The shadow of Clinton's protecting wing eventually reached Jonas Platt, the husband of a Livingston. Clinton discovered that Jonas, wanting neither protection nor favor, was able to provide for himself and knew what to do, and how to do it. After taking stock of each other they conceived a mutual respect which ultimately ripened into sincere friendship. Occasionally they quarrelled, but when Clinton showed an interest in the waterways project, this mutual goal always drew them together again.

Toward the close of 1801, De Witt Clinton strengthened his control by shrewdly appointing Morgan Lewis (brother-in-law of Chancellor Livingston) Chief Justice of the Supreme Court; also, Brockholst Livingston and Smith Thompson (the latter the husband of Sarah Livingston) Associate Justices of the Supreme Court. The clan Livingston, already immensely pleased by Clinton's goodness, throbbed with gratitude when he appointed Edward Livingston Mayor of New York City. Finally, when De Witt Clinton went to Washington and made an election-day promise of the New York electoral vote at the next presidential election, if President Jefferson would appoint Chancellor Livingston ambassador to France, and when Jefferson, mindful that the Chancellor had declined that appointment from George Washington, nevertheless offered the Chancellor the appointment, the Livingstons took Clinton to their hearts. Chancellor Livingston—who had hated Washington for denying political preferment to the entire Livingston clan and the Chief Justiceship of the Supreme Court to Chancellor Livingston—passed word down through the clan to the effect that De Witt Clinton was "in."

In 1800 crafty Aaron Burr sneaked through the State Legislature a bill granting him a charter to provide an abundance of pure water for the City of New York. Because the water from the wells at the New York street corners was polluted by drainage from outdoor privies and brackish from ocean seepage, the quality of the home brew which was produced in New York kitchens lacked "purity, body and flavor." Burr's water supply project was greeted with public acclaim until the public learned, the hard way, that the charter also authorized Burr and his associates to start a new bank in New York City and that the pure water project could not be undertaken until the bank had made enough money to finance it.

The Clintons had a bank in New York. Burr's new bank increased the competition and lowered the profits of the Clinton bank. Naturally, the Clinton family tried to get Aaron Burr over their sights. But Burr was an elusive target and as conversant with political trickery as the Clintons. However, Burr could not match them in banking. In acquiring the bank he had sacrificed the confidence of the New Yorkers. Then due to incapacity, deficient sagacity, and a Clintonian financial ambush, he lost the bank. But for Clinton's rivalry, Burr might have become the number-one man in New York State politics. So might Chancellor Livingston, if Clinton had not had the forethought to contrive his appointment as ambassador to France. For De Witt Clinton, virtue became its own handsome reward.

In 1804 Thomas Pickering, Roger Griswold, and other New England Federalists advocated the dissolution of the Union and the creation of a new republic consisting of New York, New England, and New Jersey with Burr as president, providing he could first be elected Governor of New York.

Burr was spectacular and a vote-getter, but he was shifty and by no means as likely a candidate as Supreme Court Chancellor John Lansing. From the viewpoint of Republican Party unity, Lansing was an ideal candidate for Governor because, although not a natural leader like Burr, none of the Republican factions had anything against him. At the regular Republican caucus for Governor, Burr was passed over and Lansing nominated.

Undaunted, Burr, through his admirer William P. Van Ness, contrived for himself a nomination for Governor at a caucus of dissident Republican legislators.

Lansing had consented to run, believing that a Republican candidate was as good as elected, there being no other political party strong enough to elect their own candidate. But when he learned of Burr and the Republican split, he belatedly withdrew his name. Republican party unity was already broken.

At this, the regular Republicans in caucus had to act quickly. In an emergency meeting, they nominated Morgan Lewis who was not as impeccable a character as Lansing, but he was a member of the Livingston clan and responsive to political reins.

Lewis' nomination demonstrated to Burr that the majority of the Republicans would not vote for him, but he felt sure of the backing of that dissident group of Republicans and the Federalists. However, at the moment when Burr was sure that he had the election "in the bag," Alexander Hamilton, the Great Federalist, passed the word through the Federalist party that he preferred Lewis for Governor. That settled it; Lewis was elected. To even the score, Burr killed Hamilton in a duel on July 11, 1804. By this act Burr committed political suicide.

The removal of two such nationally important figures as Hamilton and Burr created a temporary political vacuum. All of the potential candidates who sought to replace Hamilton and Burr were "longshots." Even De Witt Clinton could not have supplied Hamilton's genius for finance, nor Burr's talent for leadership. But then neither could anyone else!

In 1802 the New York Legislature rewarded Clinton by electing him to the United States Senate during the first administration of President Jefferson. Clinton was now well started on a national political career. But he made a mistake when he resigned from the Senate in 1803 to accept the mayoralty of New York City, a well-paid job padded with many attendant benefits. If Clinton had stayed in Washington and cultivated the friendship of the Southern Senators (he could be charming if he wished), he might later with their support have been elected President of the United States. Clinton preferred a bird in hand. And he like action.

For example, he assisted in the election of Morgan Lewis by rounding up that partition of the chronically unemployed usually to be found in the taprooms and sending some of them on an all-expense-paid trip to the taverns in the western counties to spread the rumor that the voters in the southern counties were strong for Lewis. Concomitantly he caused another portion to appear in the southern county taverns with the story that the western counties were solidly behind Lewis. Being to the tavern manner born, and certainly looking the part, they were able to make their stories convincing. Because communication between such widely separated areas was slow, the voters failed to discover the hoax until after the election.

Upon the election of Morgan Lewis, Associate Justice James Kent was appointed to replace him as Chief Justice of the State Supreme Court. Kent's vacancy in the Council of Appointment was filled by a young assemblyman named Daniel Tompkins, a big overgrown farm boy with a sweet disposition, a charming smile, and a keen, calculating mind.

Without consulting Clinton, Governor Lewis persuaded the Council of Appointment to appoint Maturin Livingston as Recorder of the City of New York. Clinton, thus ignored and believing that in a political sense New York City belonged to him, impulsively turned against Governor Lewis and his relatives, the Livingstons, and another feud was born.

Bad timing was Clinton's only flaw in his much publicized feud with the Livingstons. Burr's political career had ended abruptly, but his followers continued their political activities. However, they needed a leader to direct them in their voting. So tragic was the plight of those leaderless voters that De Witt Clinton's great loving heart went out to them. So deep was his sympathy and so tremulous his voice that the Burr faction joined the Clintonians—temporarily.

The Clintonians, thus augmented, became an important segment of the Republican party, although not numerous enough to have defeated the Livingston faction in an election if the Livingstons should choose to combine with the Federalists. However, the Livingston political influence was gradually declining while Clinton's was growing vigorously. But the Livingstons' power was not declining rapidly enough to satisfy Clinton. He wanted them to really toboggan, for he coveted the votes of their many followers. He also wished to secure permanently the votes of the Burr followers before some unworthy leader tried to step into Burr's political shoes.

Clinton perceived a way of appealing to Burr's followers. Because of Burr's murder of Hamilton, his followers were being snubbed. Nice people would not speak to them on the street. A newspaper titled "The American Citizen" built up an enormous circulation merely by criticizing Burr. When the editors could not think of any mean things to say about Burr which they had not already printed, the circulation slowed down. To restore it, the editorial columns looked into the private lives of Burr's followers, extending their research into the pasts of the more prominent. Immediately, the circulation took a tremendous jump. People in other cities subscribed. Burr's followers shouted for help. De Witt Clinton responded. He promised political jobs to the Burr leaders if they would round up their followers and chase them under the protecting Clintonian wing. Once Clintonians in good standing he would see to it that the newspaper let up on them.

Burr's followers were not altogether dumb. While following Burr, they had learned a thing or two about politics. Before accepting De Witt Clinton's offer, they held a meeting at Dyde's Hotel in New York. Someone suggested that if Clinton could stop the newspaper attacks by merely giving the word, perhaps he was the man accountable for them. Maybe he had created their distress so that he could relieve it. They stroked their chins, looked sidewise at each other and adjourned to meet again a few days later at Martling's beer hall.

At the Martling Hall meeting, suspicion of Clinton became a certainty. They decided to continue as a political group under a new name, "Martling Men," and as a faction in the Republican Party. In time, as the new faction gained, they dropped the Martling name because of its beer-hall connotation and took the name of Tammemund, a benevolent old Delaware Indian. As Tammemund was not an easy word to pronounce, they shortened it to "Tammany" and added the word "Society." One thing they did not change was their resentment toward Clinton for underrating their intelligence. They never forgave him for that.

During Washington's first term, Alexander Hamilton, in making federal appointments, had pushed the Livingstons to the rear like secondhand furniture, as if he were ashamed of them. The Livingstons had retaliated by bolting the party. However, when Clinton snarled at their entering his lair and making an appointment without even consulting him, they wondered what ailed him. After all, had not he recently offered jobs to Burr's followers? Those jobs could just as well have gone to his old and faithful friends, the Livingstons. As a consequence of Clinton's irascibility the Livingstons, including the Chancellor, began saying "Good morning!" to the Federalists.

By 1807 the Livingstons and the Federalists, having united in a fusion party, won a majority in the State Assembly. That majority soon elected enough Federalist Senators to the Council of Appointment to control it. Then began the exodus of Clinton's appointees and their replacement by Federalists. De Witt Clinton himself narrowly escaped walking the plank. Perhaps it was because he was stocky, broad-shouldered, beetle-browed, had a bulldog jaw, and could bite as well as growl.

Because of these and even less endearing traits, including a baleful glare, the members of the Council of Appointment were rather timid about appointing a new Mayor of New York, but it was rumored that they were considering it. The time had come for De Witt Clinton to take stock of himself, not with emotion but with candor. Would he curb his nature and try to be pleasing to everyone, or would he go on being De Witt Clinton and let other people adjust to him as best they could?

His natural approach was to bend people to his will. This procedure usually won the battle, but often lost him the war. The opposite approach, which lost battles but eventually won the support of the voters, was the gracious clasping of dirty, damp, or sticky hands, the affable patting of backs, the kissing of howling babies, and, worst of all, the agreeing with opinionated people who disagreed with him. He might endure the hands and the backs and the babies, but when it came to agreeing with people, the mere thought was abhorrent. His alternative was to find a rising, ambitious young politican who was naturally affable and gracious and gifted with the knack of attracting voters and yet who was willing to obey his orders without question or cavil. In other words, Clinton wanted a pawn whom he could move at will on the political chessboard.

Clinton found such a man in Daniel Tompkins, the Farmer's Boy. In 1797 Daniel had married the daughter of Mr. Mangle Minthorne, a wealthy New Yorker who had recently become the leader of Tammany. In 1804 Tompkins had moved up from State Assemblyman to member of the

House of Representatives at Washington and had then resigned to accept an appointment as Associate Justice of the New York State Supreme Court. Clinton had been covertly watching Tompkins. Tompkins had the qualifications of a "Friend of the People" to such a degree that there could be no holding him as long as there was a back to be slapped, or while the babies lasted. But would he obey orders after he had been elected Governor of New York State? Clinton, pondering that point, concluded that if Tompkins should rebel, he would simply unmake him. Again, Clinton had underrated the intelligence of one of his associates.

In 1807, with Clinton's backing, Daniel Tompkins was elected Governor of New York. So large was Tompkins' plurality that it became immediately obvious that he would have won without Clinton's backing. Within a year it was equally obvious that Clinton, in trying to develop a political tool, had created a Frankenstein.

In the same year, Jonas Platt was also disappointed. A vacancy occurred on the State Supreme Court bench. The Council of Appointment had considered Platt as a possibility, but gave the appointment to William W. Van Ness.*

The day following Daniel Tompkins' inauguration, the stricken United States battleship Chesapeake sailed into Norfolk Harbor. Then followed the British orders in council, Napoleon's Milan decree, and the American reply to both—the Jefferson Embargo. At first there was a fillip in the word "Embargo," like pounding on a table. The infant American nation had now matured and was demanding the respect due maturity. Unfortunately, nearly all of the goods displayed in New York stores were manufactured in foreign countries. The United States had commerce but only a few incipient industries.

The Embargo functioned, but in reverse. In a short time

*A Columbia County lawyer. Not related to William P. Van Ness the follower of Aaron Burr.

all of the wares in the New York stores had been sold. The port was closed. Only by smuggling from Canada via the Lake Champlain route could goods be imported—and then only in small quantities such as could be carried in bateaux. In protest, the New York merchants circulated a petition to have the port reopened. As the Embargo continued, tensions mounted. People became bitter and partisan. Then they became personal and called each other names.

In Albany the bitterness about the embargo engendered a collision in the social circle. Solomon Van Rensselaer was an outstanding Federalist. John Tayler, founder of the Republican-sponsored State Bank* in Albany, and equally outstanding in his own party, led the Republicans.

Because of a fancied affront to his dignity, Solomon Van Rensselaer sent a challenge to the Secretary of the Republican convention, Elisha Jenkins. Jenkins, a quiet man, who disapproved of violence, ignored the challenge. Jenkins had intended no slight, but Van Rensselaer through egotism interpreted Jenkins' silence as contempt.

A few days later Van Rensselaer observed Jenkins walking ahead of him on the street. He had a flash obsession that other people on the street and at the windows might know the story of Jenkins' refusal of his challenge and were watching to see what Mr. Solomon Van Rensselaer would do about it. Having worked himself up to a pitch, Van Rensselaer sneaked up behind Jenkins and gave him a sudden and severe caning.

Having asserted himself, Van Rensselaer, still with a chip on his shoulder continued his stroll to the State House square. There he met John Tayler and insulted him, obviously to provoke a fight. Tayler disregarded him, but Tayler's son-in-law, Dr. C. D. Cooper, probably wishing by some pleasing act to penetrate more deeply into his father-in-law's

*The present State Bank of Albany.

will, whistled to a passing friend for assistance and set about Van Rensselaer.

Bystander Governor Morgan Lewis was, like Tayler, enjoying the clobbering of the haughty Van Rensselaer. However, the odds against Van Rensselaer were so heavy that Lewis' conscience troubled him. Concluding that he should do something to even the fight, Lewis offered Van Rensselaer his cane. The offer came too late. Van Rensselaer was already down and being stamped by both Cooper and his assistant. So thoroughly was the arrogance kicked out of Van Rensselaer that he was compelled to spend the next six months in bed with the curtains drawn and there to reflect that "pride goeth before a fall"—and to damn the Embargo with all of his heart.

In central New York the farmers were loudly protesting because there was no longer a market for the flour, potash, and staves which they were accustomed to ship abroad. As a consequence they had no ready money. When wheat dropped from two dollars to seventy-five cents a bushel, Colonel Troup, agent for the Pultney estate wrote that he was having great difficulty in collecting rents. As the embargo tightened its pinch, the settlers in Oneida County turned for advice to Jonas Platt.

CHAPTER SIX

THE INTERIOR ROUTE

In addition to his official duties, a County Clerk functioned as a biographical directory for every family in his county. He also knew their aptitudes and aspirations, if any. Consequently, when Thomas Eddy in New York was appointed by the directors of the Lock Navigation Company to find an Oneida County resident who could build flood dams, he wrote to Jonas Platt.

Jonas recommended Benjamin Wright a young Connecticut Yankee, an amateur surveyor, engineer, and State Assemblyman, adding that James Geddes, a principal producer of salt at Lake Onondaga, was of equal ability as an engineer but not available. After Eddy had conferred with General Philip Schuyler, Wright was hired to build four flood dams in Wood Creek during the summer of 1802.

Flood dams were necessary because during the summer drought the flow of water in Wood Creek diminished to a mere trickle. Bateaux had to be dragged by teams of horses over the stony stream bed for a bumpy six miles from Rome to the confluence of Canada Creek because there was not enough water to float a boat.

Flood dams, by accumulating the trickle in Wood Creek, would fill within a few days. Boats going west were placed in the stream bed below the dams. When enough boats were in postion, a sluice would be opened in the lowest dam and the boats would ride down on the flood. After the westbound bateaux had passed the upstream boats which had gathered at the confluence of Wood Creek and Canada Creek, the upstream boats would be poled up to Rome on a flood released from the second dam. The other two dams were to be held in reserve.

Neither Wright nor Geddes, nor anyone else in New York State had had experience in building sluice dams, but that summer Wright, by Yankee ingenuity, devised ways to build workable flood dams.

Philip Schuyler was so pleased with them that he persuaded Eddy to concur in directing Wright to make a survey of the Mohawk River from Rome to Schenectady and to submit a plan of his own for improving the river to meet the needs of navigation.

Wright made the survey and submitted only a bare minimum of improvements. Even so, the difficulties and expenses involved were far beyond the means of the Lock Navigation Company. However, the Company had found an intelligent and resourceful man, one upon whom they could depend to carry them through an engineering emergency.

There was another man upon whom they could have depended in an emergency of another sort. He had made a great deal of money supplying rags to clothe the destitute American army at Valley Forge during the winter of 1777. Not only did he know the right people, but he somehow contrived to be on hand whenever the right people were forgathering for a round of drinks. He was convivial Gouverneur Morris, the life of any party.

One of Gouverneur Morris' favorite indoor sports was that of playing a harmless little game to keep himself amused and the public informed about him. He would permit himself to be beguiled into sitting at a tavern table with some person of importance. As soon as Morris could contrive a dramatic pause, he would utter some cryptic sentence, smile smugly, and wait for his victim to guess at the hidden meaning. That meaning would be so recondite that the guesser in desperation would afterward consult his friends about it, and they their friends. The Delphic Oracle had won publicity by a pose of inscrutability, and it still worked for Gouverneur Morris. Above all things, Morris liked to be quoted.

Throughout his political career Gouverneur Morris had been an impractical waterways enthusiast. His reliance on deductive imaginings, instead of analysis and reasoning, closed his mind to the more logical opinions of some of his experienced associates, and to certain obvious facts. Always, Morris thought of a canal as some form of improved natural waterway. He had taken that stand at the beginning. To change his views would be equivalent to admitting that he had been wrong. In his opinion such an admission would have ruined his reputation as an oracle and damaged his pride. Years later, when he had to choose between his own conception of a waterways project or a dug ditch of proper size and location, fed by streams, he clung to his own erroneous idea.

In 1803 Gouverneur Morris first revealed his concept of water transportation to Simeon De Witt, the Surveyor General of New York State. Because of his office De Witt stood just high enough to deserve the privilege of drinking with Morris when they chanced to meet one summer evening in a Schenectady tavern. If anyone else more nearly Morris' social equal had been available Gouverneur would not have lifted a stein with such borderline talent as he deemed Simeon De Witt to be, but on that particular evening it was either De Witt or a processional of lonely beers at a dull corner table. Morris reasoned that despite Simeon De Witt's social unworthiness, if he could startle De Witt about something in De Witt's own line, De Witt might quote him. Thus the evening would not be a total loss.

Because of the scarcity of newspapers the men of that time dropped in at the taverns to hear the news while drinking beer. Usually there was a round-table argument in progress which brought out current rumor and gossip. And that was the news. If a traveller from New England or the South were talking, the others would listen to the extent of ordering a second or even a third beer. If some grizzled old-timer began to "reminisce" about the olden days, they would hastily drain their glasses and depart in a body.

When Simeon De Witt, seated opposite Morris and addressing him as "Sir," asked Morris what he thought of the prospects of improving water transportation in central New York, he was not only speaking from within his province as a surveyor, but he had the attention of every customer in the room. Morris appeared to reflect until he was covertly certain that every eye was upon him and every ear extended. Then he casually remarked that the prospects depended upon whether the Lock Navigation Company would adopt his suggestion of "tapping Lake Erie and leading its waters in an artificial river directly across country to the Hudson River!"

This was certainly a new idea. Morris chuckled inwardly as he watched De Witt's astonished reaction and the customers' significant glances.

When De Witt had recovered his composure he retorted that although Lake Erie was approximately 440 feet above Hudson River tidewater, there were hills and valleys between Lake Erie and the Hudson which Mr. Morris might have overlooked.

Gouverneur Morris, after a one-glance inventory of the openmouthed yokels in the taproom, drawled:

"But my dear De Witt, *labor improbus omnia vincit.* Have you thought of that?"

De Witt replied that he had, and he agreed that "labor does overcome all obstacles," but where could money be found to pay labor for such a gigantic undertaking?

With a careless wave of his mug, Morris dismissed the argument with calm assurance, "The object will justify the labor and expense whatever it may be."

In his capacity of Surveyor General, De Witt was conversant with the topography of the military tract* of New York, but he was not familiar with the extensive lands west† of that because they were owned by large land companies who had their own surveyors, maps, and land offices. Inhibited by a training which did not permit him to make statements not based upon observation and investigation, De Witt was silent.

Unimpeded by such a nice regard for facts, Morris pressed his advantage in a tone which reached everyone in the taproom and quite a few out in the street. "The rising glories of the western world!" Forgetting what he had planned to say next, Morris drained his mug and started over again. "At no distant day the waters of the great western inland sea will, by the aid of man, break through their barriers and mingle with those of the Hudson River."

Defiantly, De Witt banged his mug on the table. "How are they going to do it?"

Regarding him reproachfully, Morris replied in a patient tone, "Numerous streams pass them through natural channels. Artificial ones might be conducted by the same routes."

Frustration dissolved De Witt's awe of Morris. He raised his voice in anger, "What do you know about Lake Erie? Have you ever been there?"

Under the misapprehension that a fist fight was about to start in the taproom, customers crowded in until it was

*Midwestern New York.

†Simeon De Witt had received drawings and topographical statistics of western New York from James Geddes. Using that information, De Witt had made an excellent map of that region in 1802. Geddes as a private individual was encouraged in his surveys for a canal route by the land companies, whereas De Witt, a State Official, had he attempted it, would have been asked to show some authority.

apparent that Morris had drawn a full house. Resolving to play to it, he said, "Why, it so happens that I have. I approached it riding along the Niagara River, a quiet, gentle stream laving the shores of a country level and fertile."

Morris observed a couple of mossy old backwoodsmen looking at him skeptically and modified his poetic description of the Niagara River. "Along the banks of this stream which, by reason of the islands in it, appears to be of moderate size, we proceeded to Fort Erie. In turning a point of the wood the lake broke on my view. I saw riding at anchor nine vessels, the least of them 100 tons. Does it seem like magic? Yet the magic is but the early efforts of victorious industry. Hundreds of large ships will at no distant period bound on the billows of those inland seas. At this point [Schenectady] commences a navigation of more than a thousand miles. Shall I lead your astonishment to the verge of incredulity? I will. Know then that one-tenth of the expense borne by Britain in the last campaign, if properly expended, would enable ships to sail from London through the Hudson River to Lake Erie. As yet, my friends, we only crawl along the outer shell of our country. The interior excels the part we inhabit in soil, climate, in everything. The proudest empire in Europe is but a bauble compared to what America will be, must be, in the course of two centuries, perhaps of one."

During this oratory De Witt, his churchwarden clay pipe gone out and his mug unnoticed, had been regarding Morris with a glassy stare. The taproom patrons had also hung upon Morris' words with a concentration unmarred by comprehension. So profoundly were they impressed that they seemed to have fallen asleep with their eyes open. De Witt looked at them, then turned to Morris who was complacently tracing a map with his finger in beer puddles on the table and pretending unawareness of the magnificence of his own rhetoric. De Witt threw his clay pipe at the back of the fireplace and his beer mug after it. Then with a scrape of his chair he arose and said, "A remarkable speech, sir, a wonderful speech! And I'll wager that you have made it so many times that you almost believe it yourself."

De Witt stamped upstairs to bed hoping to forget that speech, but he was fuming about it several days later when he reached Lake Onondaga and the salt works of his most trusted surveyor, James Geddes. In Geddes' ear he unloaded the Morris theory which, far from forgetting, he sarcastically repeated almost word for word.

To De Witt's dismay, Geddes, instead of sneering at Morris, seemed visibly impressed. He said, "Mr. De Witt, your vivid description suggests the saving of so much lockage by avoiding the descent to and the ascent from Lake Ontario that it strikes me as a grand desideratum. I have been ten years in this partly penetrated wilderness, and a knowledge of the chain of swamps which stretch across the country from the Cayuga marsh to the Mohawk River gives me an idea of the practicability of the Morris project. I shall inquire into it."

James Geddes was born and educated in Carlisle, Pennsylvania. As a young man he had paddled up the Susquehannah and its tributary, the Chemung, portaged to Seneca Lake, and descended the Seneca River to the outlet of Onondaga Lake. He had brought with him two big soap kettles for reducing brine to salt. By volunteering as a surveyor's assistant during his youth, he had picked up the rudiments of geodetics. When he could be spared from his salt works at Onondaga Lake, he travelled the forest by Indian paths east and west with stakes, measuring line and level, making observations and taking notes. From the notes he made a summary of land slopes and levels which he passed along to his friends as an hypothesis for the location of a workable canal. Obviously, a through canal which came close to Onondaga Lake would enable Geddes to ship salt both east and west in such vast quantities that he would soon become a rich man.

As Geddes turned Morris' suggestion over in his mind, it became an obsession. He corresponded with land agents and surveyors, seeking maps and any information which they could give about the topography of central New York.

At first Geddes' friends tried to avoid him. Then they ceased to be his friends. But a habit once started is not easily broken. Geddes continued grasping their buttonholes in the manner of the Ancient Mariner and pouring out his fixation, sparing no details. By resolution and persistence he eventually developed a few enthusiastic, loud-spoken protagonists. Not that his protagonists really agreed with Geddes, or even believed in his obsession, but they could not bring themselves to agree with those who disagreed. They were men of principle and their pride would not let them.

By 1807, when the Onondaga country had been set off as Onondaga County, James Geddes and his friends were feverishly talking about a canal with anyone who would listen. Their fervency was contagious. It spread faster than Genesee Fever, and differed from it mainly in that people once infected with "canal fever" seldom recovered. Like Geddes, they talked about it whenever they could find a listener.

Eventually, those who disagreed with Geddes had become so involved with his supporters that their dispute warmed up to feud proportions. Then Joshua Forman, a Union College graduate, a lawyer and a convincing speaker, entered the argument with a bugle note. Why not have a survey made to prove the practicability of a cross-country canal? The survey would cost money? And there had been previous surveys? Of course, but why not petition the Legislature for an appropriation to survey this newly proposed route?

Among the voters the petitioning of the Legislature for an appropriation for almost anything, even a survey for a canal, rang the bell. Those who were skeptical of the project or opposed to the bell-ringer were nevertheless charmed by the music. Forman was a Federalist in the Republican County of Onondaga. Nevertheless, on a fusion, called the "Canal Ticket," he won the April 1807 election to the State Assembly with only two voters in his own town dissenting.

Relaxing after the excitement of feuding, people in the western counties began to wonder what they had been fighting about. Slowly it dawned on them that it was not necessary to live on the banks of a natural stream to enjoy water transportation for their farm produce. A canal could be dug right to anyone's door and made to connect with other dug canals tributary to the Hudson River. Ocean-going vessels floated on the Hudson at Albany.

While the unbelievers were adjusting to this awakening, Jesse Hawley of Canandaigua published in the *Ontario Messenger* a series of enlightened articles on the advantages of a dug canal, east and west across central New York, which would not even approach Lake Ontario except by a lateral ditch terminating at Oswego. *Those articles marked the transition of public thinking from a natural waterways project to that of a dug canal.*

By February 4, 1808, Forman, having taken his seat in the Assembly, joined a small clique of faithful canal supporters formed within the group of advocates of transportation by natural waterways. The water transportation group was headed by Gouverneur Morris. Mr. Gold of Whitestown, a friend of Jonas Platt, was an influential member of the clique.

In the assembly room of the new State Capitol on Pinkster Hill in Albany the temperature on that February morning may have been as high as 38° Farenheit. Because the building was of brick and stone and heated only by big fireplaces, the interior was smoky and penetratingly damp. However, the thick walls did shut out the wind, which was more than could be said of the homes of many of the Assemblymen. But the temperature of the Assembly Chamber was of no concern to the Assembly. They were too excited by the heat of debate to notice the cold. Only Joshua Forman looked cold. He was pale. He trembled slightly, but from nervousness rather than chill. He knew that after the motion then under debate had been voted upon and the count had been taken, it would be his privilege to make the next motion.

As Forman listened to the overtones of arguments based on doubtful evidence and questionable assertions, and the undertones of specious reasoning and bald opinion, he quaked inwardly. He was a modest, unobtrusive man who dreaded making an exhibition of himself. The speech which he had carefully prepared was logical, and not at all emotional. Compared to the full-throated oratory which had been reverberating through the Chamber, he feared that his effort would seem flat and dull.

All too soon a vote was called. The Speaker's gavel rapped. Joshua Forman took the floor. In a spasm of stage fright, only partially controlled, his hands fumbled with his notes. Then the orderly thinking of his college-trained mind responded. Step by step, he recalled the futile attempts, the faltering, stumbling failure to so improve the rivers and streams that bulky freight might be transported—not by the hundredweight—but by the ton!

He spoke of another groping effort, the turnpikes. Freight wagons were carrying modest loads and struggling to maintain regular schedules on inferior roadbeds and steep hills over which they could never hope to move greater weight than they were now hauling.

He declared in his quiet forceful manner "If your State—our Country—is to grow, transportation must grow with it to make this development possible."

The Chamber was hushed. All eyes were upon him. "Why?" he wondered. Then his subconscious supplied the answer. He had been elected in a bipartisan county on a fusion ticket. So far as he knew his had been the first and the only fusion ticket in western New York. The very nature of the upstate voters was not to fuse but to fight! Nothing like it had ever happened before; such a success was without political precedent. Therefore, to him was now being given the opportunity to convince this Assembly of what must be done.

In a quiet tone, become vibrant with reserve power, Forman offered this resolution: "That a joint committee be appointed to take into consideration the propriety of causing an accurate survey to be made of the most eligible and direct route for a canal to open communication between the Hudson River and Lake Erie and that Congress be induced to appropriate such sums as may prove necessary to the accomplishment of that object."

Joshua Forman paused and looked hopefully about for approving glances. Instead, there was a general shaking of heads and a murmur of derision partly smothered by coughing. Forman tried to speak, choked, then with an effort launched into his plea. The general subject of canals and its application to a State canal and the topography of central New York rolled out in words that seemed to spring from his lips. He spoke of following the Mohawk Valley to Rome and the Oneida Valley and the Seneca River to the head of Mud Creek.

Forman turned his focus westward, speaking familiarly of a route beside the Niagara River, up the Tonawanda Valley and down Allen's Creek to the Genesee River. In summing up, he estimated the cost of building such a canal at ten million dollars, but dismissed the figure as a trifle compared to the value of the resultant improvement in transportation and the added commerce it would accommodate. There was no derision when Forman stopped speaking. He sat down amid a tribute of silence: not the momentary hush of curiosity, but the profound stillness of deep reflection.

By a tap of his gavel the Speaker opened debate on the resolution. There was only silence. Forman's factual appeal, devoid of all emotion, had not been notable as oratory, but it had provoked thought. After a suitable pause the gavel tapped for a vote. The Assembly's next reaction judged by their mutters and whispers was to the effect that "The measures couldn't do any harm, and it might do some good."

The resolution was voted favorably in the Assembly. On March 21, Mr. Gold from the Joint Committee reported the resolution so amended as to order the Surveyor General "to cause an accurate survey to be made of the streams in the usual route* of communication between the Hudson River and Lake Erie and *such other contemplated route as he may deem proper* . . . of which one copy shall be filed with the Secretary of State and another transmitted to the President of the United States."

The Senate concurred on April 6. On April 11, 1808, six hundred dollars were appropriated to enable the Surveyor General to carry out the resolution.

On June 11 Simeon De Witt, the Surveyor General, authorized James Geddes to make the survey. In effect, De Witt's letter was an order to resurvey the old bateau route, the route of the Lock Navigation Company which, as a practical route for transporting bulky freight, had proved worthless. It included locking around Niagara Falls and cruising to Oswego over the heavy swell against the southern shore of Lake Ontario. Still more locks would be required to ascend the Oswego River, especially at Oswego Falls, to reach the level of Oneida Lake.

Forman knew that such a survey would be merely a repetition of a past blunder. Simeon De Witt knew it, and so

*The usual route was the old bateau route.

did Geddes. So far as any benefit to transportation was concerned, none was intended. The passing of the Forman resolution had been merely a salute by the Assembly to an Assemblyman who had cornered every vote in his own town but two. Fortunately, the clique in the Joint Committee had already contributed a hope of success by adding that rider "and such other contemplated route as he may deem proper."

In his order to Geddes, De Witt admitted that the appropriation did not provide enough money to survey any route other than the one specified, but he insinuated that if Geddes wished to explore the practicability of a route from Lake Erie to Rome by way of Tonawanda Creek, the Genesee and the Seneca Rivers at his own expense, he could consider that he had the authority to do so. Without hope of personal profit or prestige, Elkanah Watson had given his best to promote water transportation; Philip Schuyler had endured the rigors of winter constructing locks in the Mohawk River at Little Falls. Platt, Forman, and De Witt had been equally devoted. James Geddes was a man after this same pattern. He executed the survey ordered, knowing that it was useless. Afterward, although winter was upon him, he availed himself of the authority to make that survey which he had so long wished to make. That this would involve serving the State on his own time and at his own expense without hope of return was to Geddes of minor consequence.

On February 22, 1822, Mr. Geddes wrote a letter describing his explorations in 1808 when he had searched the wilderness of western New York seeking natural streams of an elevation sufficient to supply water for filling locks, so that heavily laden boats could be lifted or lowered to a different level. To keep heavy traffic moving in a dug canal, this abundant supply of water from higher elevations would be essential. If he could not find streams at high elevations, there would be no canal. In a later letter Geddes wrote:

"The spot of great difficulty and uncertainty respecting our inland route remained unexamined—the tract between the Genesee River and Palmyra or headwaters of Mud Creek and the hopes, from a view of maps, were discouraging indeed. Where is the water to be got for locking over the high land that was supposed to rise between Genesee River and Mud Creek. All knowledge of an interior route was incomplete while this piece of country remained unknown.

"In December of that year I again left home for the above object and after discovering at the west end of Palmyra that singular brook which divides, running part to Oswego and part to Irondequot Bay, I levelled from this spot to the Genesee River and to my great surprise and joy found the level of the river elevated far above the spot where the brooks part and no high lands between. But to make the Genesse River run down Mud Creek it must be got over the Irondequot Valley. After leveling from my first line one and a half mile up the valley I found the place where the canal is now making across the stream.

"The passage of the Irondequot Valley is on a surface not surpassed in the world for singularity. The ridges along the top of which the canal is carried are in many places of just sufficient height and width for support. When the work is finished the appearance to a stranger will be that nearly all of those natural embankments are artificial works. The surface of the foundation of the arch for the stream to pass through is just seventy feet below the top water line of the canal."

The great obstacle had been looked for between the Genesee River and the waters of the Seneca. The discovery of the passage of the Irondequot Valley really solved the whole question.

James Geddes made his discoveries in primeval forest where few, if any, white men had ever set foot. He slept on leaves heaped between logs. He clubbed porcupines for food. When it snowed or rained he got wet. This expense amounting to $73 came from his own pocket. However, his hardships paid off for his report proved conclusively that a canal could be dug from Lake Erie eastward to the Seneca River. In accordance with the provisions of the Forman resolution, a copy of that report with a topographic sketch by Geddes was sent to President Jefferson.

The route traced in the Geddes' sketch deserved Jefferson's approval because it ultimately became the route of the Erie Canal. However, to make sure that Jefferson would condescend to look at the report and, having looked at it, comprehend it, required that a proponent of the canal go to Washington, call upon the President and persuade him to take the papers out of a pigeonhole. It was a fair assumption that Jefferson would be reluctant to do so, but again it seemed to Forman that "to him it had been given." It was January, 1809. The long journey by stage would be uncomfortable and cold, but the canal clique in the Assembly thought that he should go. Forman's conscience confirmed their urging.

When Forman had presented his resolution to the Assembly, he had repeated that portion of Jefferson's recent message to Congress in which the President had recommended "that the (Federal) Treasury surplus over and above such sums as could be applied to extinguishing the national debt, be appropriated to the opening of canals and the construction of turnpikes."

Jefferson's reputation as an orator caused the clique to doubt not only the President's sincerity, but his receptivity to a plea from the New York Legislature that he divert even a small portion of the national surplus toward building a canal for New York State. However, that doubt would have to be supported by the President's actual refusal before the subject of inland water transportation could again be mentioned in the State Legislature.

As soon as arrangements had been completed for his introduction to the President, Forman with cold hands and even colder feet started for Washington.

Two frigid, weary weeks later Forman arrived in Washington. After the custom of that period, he immediately wrote a letter to his contact requesting an appointment with Jefferson. The next morning the contact called at the hotel, took Forman by the arm, marched him several blocks down the street to the White House, pointed at the door, said "G'wan in," and left him. Thrown thus upon his own resources, Forman's slender self-confidence also departed.

Steeling himself for the ordeal, Forman climbed the slippery steps and gingerly lifted the knocker. He was instantly admitted by a bowing Negro butler. President Jefferson himself came out into the hall and helped him to take off his greatcoat. By the time they were seated before the fire in the President's study Forman's self-confidence had returned plus some that he did not know that he had.

At Jefferson's request, Forman stated his mission, then launched into the particulars. In his usual low earnest tone, Forman briefly described Geddes' successful survey. At this, a lingering smile left Jefferson's face indicating to Forman that he had caught the President's attention. Forman referred to the map of the canal route which had been sent to the White House. Jefferson's brow clouded slightly, but he said nothing. Forman touched lightly on the means of overcoming certain problems of construction, then let himself go on the subject of the advantages and benefits which the canal would bring to the country at large. He concluded by emphasizing the necessity of such a canal for building up a frontier defense and for transporting troops and supplies in time of war.

The rapt attention with which Jefferson had followed his presentation of the canal story, step by step, caused Forman to feel that he had spoken convincingly. After Forman had stopped talking, the President remained plunged in abstraction.

Forman was beginning to feel hopeful when Jefferson came out of his brown study and admitted that it sounded like a very fine project and might be executed a century hence. He added, "Why sir, here is a canal but a few miles long projected by General Washington, which, if completed, would render this city which has languished for many years, a fine commercial city. The small sum of two hundred thousand dollars necessary to complete it cannot be obtained from the general government, the state government, or from individuals. And you, sir, talk of making a canal 350 miles through the wilderness! It is little short of madness to think of it at this day."

Forman was bitterly disappointed. He tried to be cheerful as well as polite as he bowed himself out. Jefferson was equally polite. Indeed, Forman on his gloomy journey back to Albany had only the consoling thought that he had at least achieved the ultimate in polite refusals.

Meanwhile, the people of New York State were becoming restless because of the Jefferson embargo. Stagnated shipping and commerce had generated a full scale financial depression. With characteristic unpredictability De Witt Clinton who had violently opposed the embargo, became overnight in favor of it. While his friends were still fighting the embargo in the belief that they were doing what Clinton wanted them to do, Clinton introduced in the State Legislature a resolution approving the embargo, the administration, and the prospective Madison administration. He even went so far as to make a speech blaming the Federalists for their opposition to the embargo.

This was De Witt Clinton profundo. Even his admirers like Jonas Platt arose in protest. Platt effectively answered Clinton in the State Senate, knowing that he had the backing of a large number of Federalists who had emigrated from New England to western New York. In the Assembly, Abraham Van Vechten, noted for his sarcasm, told off Clinton. Apparently Clinton was under the illusion that he held the balance of power, never suspecting that the remnant of the Burr faction and the followers of Morgan Lewis would join the Federalists, but they did. In the April election they swept the State. When the Assembly convened in January, Clinton was powerless and almost without influence. On the other hand, Platt, in the same election, had been voted State Senator from the western district.

Neither an embargo nor a constitutional amendment could completely check the interchange of trade goods. President Jefferson sat smiling at his desk in Washington, content with the idea that his embargo had been effective. But as American merchant vessels with full cargoes slipped nightly out of New England ports and more and more laden bateaux were poled down the Richelieu River into Canada, the Jefferson smile faded while the presidential brow suffused with red. Plainly the embargo could be only partially enforced. On March 1, 1809, over Jefferson's remonstrance, Congress ended the fourteen-months-old farce by repealing the embargo.

The embargo was a failure, but it was also a turning point in American destiny. After 1809 the people in the northeastern states became industrial-minded. At last they had come to realize that the United States could not maintain itself as a world power without industry. That was plain to all. A few of the more intelligent and far-seeing also perceived that domestic industry could not prosper without adequate transportation for heavy goods. In other words they could not develop industry without canals.

CHAPTER SEVEN

CHALLENGE OF THE UNCONQUERED

By 1810 the Republican voters in central New York had become acutely aware that despite their increased crops and the abundant waterpower available for manufacturing, they were economically stagnant and would continue in that frustration until they could do something about transportation. The Republicans in New York City and the Hudson Valley, having deep-water transportation, were not the least bit interested in the plight of central New York. The State Legislature was, as usual, indifferent to the problems of a small, and rather distant, portion of the voters.

Because the Republican nominee for governor would obviously be Daniel Tompkins to succeed himself, the central New Yorkers had generally agreed to bolt the Republican party and nominate their own candidate. At the January 5, 1810 convention of the Federalist party in Albany, an impressive number of Republicans appeared and joined the Federalists in nominating for State Governor on the Federalist ticket—Jonas Platt.

The complacent Republican leaders had not suspected that the frontier voters were so unified and determined. Those voters were supposed to be loyal Republicans, regardless of whether the Legislature paid them any attention. Their fusion with the Federalists mortified the Republican leaders. Further mortification resulting from another fusion was about to rock those complacent men.

When the State Legislature convened on January 30, 1810,

A DURHAM BOAT FORCING A RIFT— *R. A. GRIDER*

". . . the crew wading and pushing the Craft through the pass.

"Sometimes ropes were attached and men on shore pulled and aided in going forward. If they failed they awaited the coming of another boat, when both crews assisted in forcing a passage.

"By means of stones placed, as here shown, the water at shoal places was diverted to one point and sufficient in depth for a boat to pass."

BEGINNING OF THE SALT WORKS AT ONONDAGA LAKE

HOUSE OF JUDGE WHITE, WHITESTOWN

THE BINNEKILL AS SEEN FROM THE SCHENECTADY RIVER BRIDGE
R. A. GRIDER, 1898
(Buildings restored from evidence of aged citizens of Schenectady)

"Inland Navigation Boats are starting out on their way westward, up the Mohawk, toward which they are sailing. Navigation began in 1795 & ended in 1825. . . ."

ELKANAH WATSON

PHILIP SCHUYLER

GOUVERNEUR MORRIS

THE PORT OF BUFFALO, 1815

THOMAS EDDY

JAMES KENT
DANIEL TOMPKINS
SMITH THOMPSON
UTICA
Whitesboro
Oriskany Cr.
Sedaghqueda Cr.
Nail Cr.
Ballows Cr.
Clarks Cr.
Fergusons Cr.
Myers Cr.
Great Wes
Turnpike
Cooperstown
Otsego Lake

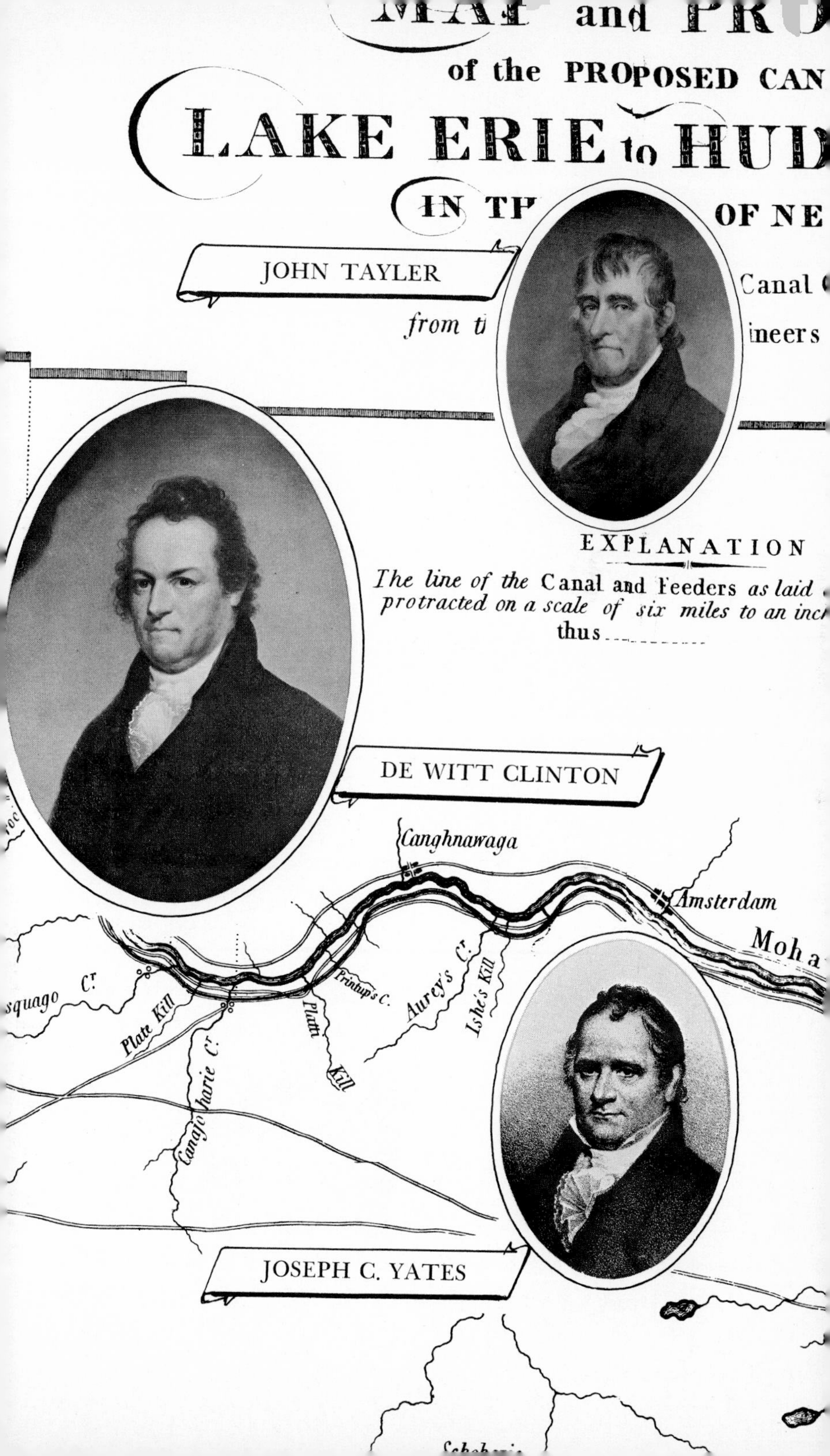
and
of the PROPOSED CAN
LAKE ERIE to HUD
IN TH
OF NE
JOHN TAYLER
Canal
from t
ineers
EXPLANATION
The line of the Canal and Feeders as laid
protracted on a scale of six miles to an inc
thus
DE WITT CLINTON
Canghnawaga
Amsterdam
Moha
squago Cr
Plate Kill
Canajoharie Cr
Platt Kill
Printup's C.
Aurey's Cr
Ishe's Kill
JOSEPH C. YATES

INTERIOR OF A TAVERN BAR ROOM ON THE MOHAWK TURNPIKE

R. A. GRIDER, 1897

"Interior of the Chauncey Jerome Tavern Bar Room, one of the Mohawk Turnpike stopping places. In later times it was a place where hunters and fishermen came for sport."

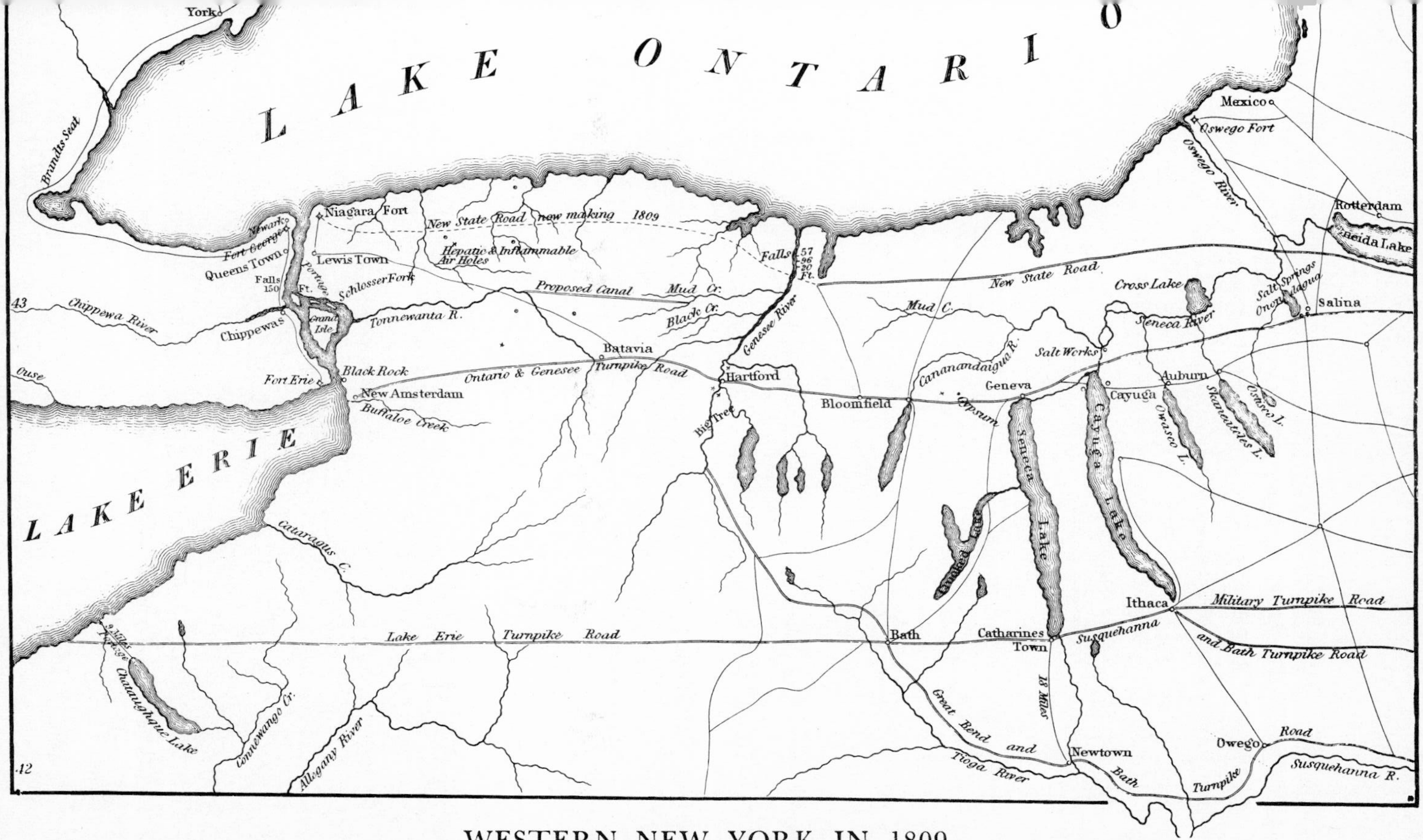

LAKE ONTARIO
York
Brandts Seat
Mexico
Oswego Fort
Oswego River
Rotterdam
Oneida Lake
Newark
Fort George
Queens Town
Falls 150 Ft.
Portage
Niagara Fort
Lewis Town
Schlosser Fork
New State Road now making 1809
Hepatic & Inflammable Air Holes
Proposed Canal
Mud Cr.
Black Cr.
Falls 57 96 20 Ft.
New State Road
Cross Lake
Salt Springs
Onondagua
Salina
43
Chippewa River
Chippewas
Grand Isle
Tonnewanta R.
Mud C.
Seneca River
Salt Works
Ouse
Fort Erie
Black Rock
Batavia
Ontario & Genesee Turnpike Road
Genesee River
Hartford
Cananandaigua R.
Geneva
Cayuga
Auburn
Owasco L.
Skaneateles L.
Ostisco L.
New Amsterdam
Buffaloe Creek
Bloomfield
Gypsum
Big Tree
Seneca Lake
Cayuga Lake
Crooked Lake
LAKE ERIE
Cataragus C.
Ithaca
Military Turnpike Road
Lake Erie Turnpike Road
Bath
Catharines Town
Susquehanna and Bath Turnpike Road
9 Miles Portage
Chataughque Lake
Connewango Cr.
Allegany River
18 Miles
Great Bend and Bath Turnpike Road
Newtown
Owego
Tioga River
Susquehanna R.
42

WESTERN NEW YORK IN 1809

SENATE CHAMBER, OLD CAPITOL

ASSEMBLY CHAMBER, OLD CAPITOL

JUSTICE'S COURT IN THE BACKWOODS, 1850—*T. H. MATTESON*

STATE STREET, ALBANY, 1805—*JAMES EIGHTS*

COHOES FALLS, ON THE MOHAWK RIVER—*JACQUES MILBERT*

the all-important Council of Appointment consisted of two Federalists and two Republicans. With Republican Governor Tompkins casting a vote to break any tie, and Republicans already holding enough appointive offices to give them political control of the State, it appeared that the Republican party had the situation in the bag.

Then as today, when any politican or party had control of the electorate, there was a tendency toward complacency. Haughtiness dulled the fine edge of caution. Peremptory orders were passed down through the ranks. The dissident, and even those who were rather slow about executing orders, were disciplined.

Robert Williams, Republican State Senator and member of the Council of Appointment, had somehow failed to meet the expectations of the hand that had made him—politically. Secretly apprised that "The Hand" had resolved to "unmake" him, and knowing that he wouldn't be given a chance to present his side of the case to impartial ears, and that he would be dropped from politics as soon as his term had expired, Williams yielded to a compulsive urge to retaliate before rather than after he had been kicked out.

To everyone's astonishment Williams suddenly began voting with the Federalists in the Council of Appointment. This gave the Federalists a three-to-one majority and precluded Governor Tompkins' casting vote.

Scarcely able to believe their ears, the two Federalist members of the Council tentatively voted to replace with Federalists a few Republican officeholders. Williams voted with them and, without actual commitment, contrived to convey the thought that he hoped that they would replace more Republicans—many more.

Then began the great exodus of Republican officeholders, which did not terminate until the rug had been pulled from beneath all Republicans within the jurisdiction of the Council of Appointment and their easy chairs had been filled by

Federalists. One of the last to be relieved of office was Senate Majority Leader (also the Mayor of New York) De Witt Clinton. With head bowed and shoulders bent, Clinton walked sadly down the steps into the street muttering, "They can't do this to me."

When the turmoil had subsided, one thing was clear. The weakness in the policy-making structure as revealed by Williams' defection could not be corrected without abolishing the powerful Council of Appointment. Naturally no one wanted to undertake such a revolutionary measure.

Governor Daniel Tompkins, an outspoken believer in military preparedness, and a political opportunist, suggested in a speech to the State Senate that in the insurgency of Senator Robert Williams there was a lesson for the voters. He declared that in the future the Republican and Federalist parties should unite to support the State government in matters of military preparedness. The effect of Tompkins' speech was the reverse of what he had expected. Instead of providing a solution, it contributed the "last straw." At that time the fissure between political parties was so deep that the shifting from one political party to another was called an apostasy, equivalent to the total desertion from one's religious faith. The fall of man was the first apostasy. The revolt of the Republicans to support Jonas Platt for governor was another, and considered comparable. Naturally a reaction followed.

Thomas Jefferson had successfully broken the restrictive and coercive hold which the Federalist one-party regime had laid upon the United States. Was that achievement to be nullified in New York State by a reversion to a one-party rule, born of a fusion for defense? Especially when there was no war? If they had to return to a one-party condition, they would all be expected to agree on main issues. The next step might be a monarchy. The complacency of the Republican senators gave way to agitation.

Upon further reflection, the Senators became so unnerved by the upstate apostasy that they debated the question of whether the Senate should even reply to Governor Tompkins' speech about a fusion. The subject of their debate was so unusual that it aroused an extraordinary amount of public interest. Taking advantage of the general confusion and of the rule which gave every Senator the privilege of expounding his views, Jonas Platt delivered several rousing but scarcely relevant speeches about the virtues of the Federalist party and the things for which they stood, such as conservatism and commerce and Platt for Governor.

Senator John Tayler surmised that Platt had overplayed his hand. He countered with a vicious attack on Platt and the rest of the Federalists, denouncing them as pro-British Tories. In a calculated emotional outburst Tayler falsely accused the Federalists of including men who, during the Revolution, had assisted the Indians in massacring Americans. A Federalist senator, Daniel Parrish, then spoke in support of Jonas Platt. Whereupon Tayler, with fine sarcasm, narrated the scalping of Parrish senior at Cherry Valley and feigned horror at finding the son of so illustrious a Tryon County soldier advocating the Tory cause on the floor of the State Senate.

During his days of fur trading with the Indians John Tayler had learned the importance of timing. As an interpreter at Indian Councils he had picked up some of the fundamentals of impassioned oratory. He had learned to recognize when an antagonist was in the act of making a false step or erroneous statement and at what point to attack to turn that error to his own advantage. In this hard school Tayler had developed his lifelong obsession—the desire for money and power. A year or so after the Revolution Tayler had settled in Albany, opened a store, and became an anti-Federalist, because like certain other storekeepers he envied the wealthy aristocracy.

In 1800, when Jefferson consolidated the anti-Federalists with the Republican Party, Tayler became a Republican. In 1803, when Elkanah Watson called Tayler's attention to the two Federalist banks in Albany and the complete lack of a Republican bank, Tayler perceived his long-sought opportunity to become both wealthy and politically prominent. That September Tayler opened the State Bank of Albany and began a steady ascent to wealth and a top spot in the Republican party of New York.

By 1810 Tayler had acquired both wealth and political power, but he was no apostate. Once a Republican, always a Republican. He held no animosity toward Platt as a man, but since Platt was the Federalist candidate for Governor, Tayler felt it his duty to oppose Platt in upholding Tompkins, the Republican nominee. Therefore, when Platt made his incautious speeches in the Senate, Tayler gave Platt "the works."

Tayler's speech against Platt, although it twisted the truth and misrepresented the facts, produced a state-wide strong emotional reaction against the Federalist party. At Platt's expense Tayler gained in stature as a Republican leader.

Tayler was a hard man, but he did have a conscience. Because he had seriously injured Platt who had never harmed him, Tayler's conscience bothered him. Eventually he developed a personal hatred for Platt because he had hurt him.

To offset Tayler's successful attack, Jonas Platt was tempted to introduce the canal project as a part of his campaign. Forman, by using it in Onondaga County, had won a seat in the Assembly. However, there were several counties strongly against the canal. Daniel Tompkins, as Governor, had become more popular than ever. Jonas anticipated that his own vote margin, if any, would be slim. If the canal should fail to pull him through in the election, he would drag the canal down to defeat—and more ridicule. Platt's final decision was to keep the canal out of partisan politics until some far stronger candidate favorable to the canal could carry the issue through to certain victory.

By March 12, 1810, adjournment of the Legislature was approaching. That evening Jonas was sitting before the fire in the back bedroom which he occupied in the home of James Bleecker, the father-in-law of his younger brother Charles. He would have been more than welcome in the family circle downstairs, but he wanted to be alone. In his mind he was analyzing his fellow senators, their commitments and their quarrels. It seemed to him that there must be some way to divert their attention from petty partisan animosities long enough to consider construction of the canal by the State. Since President Jefferson had refused Federal aid, no present alternative remained.

A maid tapped at his door and said that there was a gentleman downstairs to see him. As Jonas went down the broad, carpeted stairway he saw standing under the twinkling glass of the candlelighted chandelier, cane in one hand, beaver and muffler in the other, and with his greatcoat thrown back—Thomas Eddy.

Jonas greeted him joyfully. James Bleecker and Charles Platt entering the hall from the living room were so impressed when Jonas introduced them to Eddy that they became inarticulate. They knew Eddy to be a director of the Lock Navigation Company, a prominent speculator, one of the wealthiest men in New York, and a noted philanthropist. It had never occurred to them that he was devoted to Jonas.

Later, alone before the fire in the snug privacy of Jonas' room, sipping a Dempsey Slater spiced, hot-buttered rum, Thomas Eddy confided, "Jonas, do you know that the Lock Navigation Company is quietly seeking legislative authority to explore western New York for the purpose of extending navigation from Oneida Lake to Seneca Lake?"

When Eddy paused to observe the effect of his remark, Jonas leaned forward and took a hickory splinter from the wood basket. Holding it at either end, he bent it as though testing its strength. Eddy watched him a moment, then repeated his question.

Jonas asked, "Thomas, how far do you think this splinter will bend before it breaks?"

Eddy frowned, "Jonas, why don't you answer my question?"

Jonas bent the splinter into a bow. "Because, Thomas, when you answer my question you will also answer your own."

Eddy said with affected patience, "If you bend it any farther, it will snap. Throw it in the fire. It has no part in our discussion."

Jonas bent the splinter a bit more. It snapped. Tossing it into the fire, he said "Neither has the Lock Navigation Company. Further westward exploration would place greater strain on their already depleted treasury. Another extension of their inadequate waterway might so involve the company that it would break like that splinter."

Eddy gripped Platt's knee. "But Jonas, this is the Lock Navigation Company's darkest hour. If we can extend the channel only as far as Onondaga Lake, twenty-five thousand tons of salt, more or less, which now passes down the Oswego River to be transferred to Canadian schooners at Oswego will then float eastward on the Lock Navigation Company's route to Schenectady. Philadelphia and New York can stop importing salt from Bermuda. Financed by increasing lock fees, the Company should then be able to extend their navigation to Catherinestown at the head of Seneca Lake, portage to the Chemung, and portage again from Canisteo to the Alleghany River. Why Jonas, if the Lock Navigation Company can tap that salt mine we shall be distributing New York salt, and other things too, clear down the Ohio River to Kentucky!"

Jonas shook his head obstinately, "No, you won't."

"Why not?"

"Because you'll be floating that salt down natural streams, all subject to flood, drought, and uprooted, drifting trees. If the water is high, the current is too strong for heavily-laden upstream boats. If it's low, there isn't enough water in the rifts to float a boat carrying a full cargo without danger of capsizing."

Eddy looked straight at Platt. "Jonas you're unreasonable! Hundreds of tons are carried on the Mohawk River every summer."

Looking into the fire, Jonas shook his head "Some yes, but nowadays most of it is hauled by big-wheeled wagons on the turnpikes. And you know it."

Eddy regarded Jonas reproachfully. "I've always considered you a loyal friend of the canal."

Jonas arose and jerked the bell-pull. "I *am* friendly to a workable plan for a dug canal or ditch to be supplied by natural streams which will maintain a constant water level in the canal. But an unpredictable, uncontrollable river like the Mohawk is not a canal and in our time it never will be."

Eddy compressed his lips, reflecting.

Dempsey Slater, responding to the bell-pull, entered with a steaming pitcher and a tray with glasses, lemons, and spice bowl. A rising wind rattled ice particles against the windows. They sat in silence while Slater served the rum and piled logs on the fire until it crackled. When he had done everything he could to make them comfortable, he quietly withdrew.

Eddy pointed his tall glass at Jonas. "How far would you dig that ditch?"

"From the Hudson River to Lake Erie. Following a nearly level route, the distance would be about three hundred and fifty-five miles."

"Through howling wilderness!"

Jonas smiled. "After the howls of derision which we are bound to hear before we can start digging, the 'howling' of the wilderness will be a blessed relief."

"But a ditch that long would cost millions. Who can say how many. Where would you get the money?"

Jonas took a swallow of rum. "I was sitting here pondering that very question when you came. Frankly, I don't know."

"Perhaps a shorter ditch, say from the Hudson to Seneca Lake, might be the solution."

Jonas shook his head. "Thomas, you just don't know the value of that western country. The resources of the soil south and west of Lake Erie are as vast as the Lake itself. Why settle for anything less?"

Eddy's eyes sparkled. "You mean that if the canal isn't built the entire distance, it isn't worth making a start? Jonas, that's what I like about you. And you're the one to lead the cause. Why not present your ideas to the Legislature? Yank that bell-pull, get quills, ink, and paper and we'll lay out a plan of procedure."

Slater answered the bell and soon returned with writing materials and more rum. He thoughtfully moved the table closer to the fire, arranged the paper and inkhorn with care, then said proudly, "Mr. Platt, if you need me, pull the bell-cord. I'll be waiting in the kitchen all night."

After Slater had gone, Eddy said, "Pick up that quill, Jonas. Let's draft a resolution to investigate the possibilities of a dug canal between Lake Erie and the Hudson River."

For hours they bent over the sketching of a resolution authorizing a survey for a dug canal, while intermittent hail lashed the window panes. The room grew cold. The candles guttered and burned low. Without being summoned, Slater appeared with more firewood, new candles, hot rum, and an encouraging smile.

By dawn they had completed the resolution. To prove

that the resolution was nonpartisan, without actually stating it in the text, they appended a list of suggested canal commissioners. The names included the wealthy and influential in both parties.

Platt, gray-faced with fatigue, read aloud his fourth and final draft, free at last of corrections and deletions. He concluded by remarking "There's one more problem—the most important of all. Who will sponsor this resolution?"

Eddy yawned. "You, of course."

Jonas shook his head. "I haven't enough political strength. Indeed no Federalist in the Legislature has the following and the tactfulness to win the approval of both houses for such a controversial measure."

Eddy arose and stood with his back to the fire. "Tactfulness? Hum! Can you name a prominent man in the Legislature who is tactful?"

"Yes. Daniel Tompkins. He is noted for his tact."

"So he is. And he's aggressive too. But he's not a fighter. People like him, but they're not afraid of him. He'll rise to heights in the Republican party, but he won't stay there because he's not pugnacious. Therefore he's not a true leader."

Platt shrugged wearily, rested his elbows on the table and buried his face in his hands.

Eddy looked out of the window at the rapidly increasing daylight. After a long silence, he remarked quietly, "As morning dawns and the trees and roofs are taking shape, I know that in one of those houses lies sleeping the man for whom we are looking. Probably he has never dreamed of such a thing as a dug canal from Lake Erie to the Hudson. But when you expound the canal plan to him, Jonas, as you explained it to me, he will feel the challenge of the unconquered wilderness. And because he must see in the project a political future, he will accept the dare. I wonder how long it will take us to find him."

Jonas looked up blinking. "*If* we find him."

Eddy gathered up his coattails so that the fire could warm the backs of his legs. "Oh, we'll find him. He's someone in the Legislature."

Jonas sat up and started tearing the first three drafts of the resolution. "If he's in the Legislature, that settles it. There isn't a senator or an assemblyman who would risk offering this resolution, or for that matter any resolution, without first getting De Witt Clinton's approval. And I know that Clinton would never give it. His uncle, the governor, was dead set against the canal, although he never openly admitted it."

Eddy snapped his fingers. "You've named him!"

"Named whom?"

"The man we're looking for."

Jonas stared, "Clinton?—But Thomas, Clinton is not our man. He has so many enemies. And he's making more every day."

Eddy poured the last of the rum into the glasses. "Jonas, my friend, you underestimate Clinton. For that matter so does nearly everyone else. He has the most fascinating personality of any man in the State. As for his enemies, he could convert every one of them into a friend if he wished to make the effort. But he doesn't try because above all else he loves a fight, any kind of a fight. And he fights to win. However he has another side. He is highly educated, uses the most telling and graceful rhetoric I have ever heard. He can be gracious and utterly charming. Like any Irishman he wants to be boss. That's his dominant characteristic. Beneath it all he's absolutely fearless. Can't you see what the challenge of the wilderness would mean to such a man?"

Jonas reflectively sipped his rum. "Yes, Thomas, I also know that Clinton can be agreeable when——"

"When he has something to gain by it? Isn't that what you are about to say?"

Jonas nodded.

Eddy grinned. "In your opinion, just how agreeable were Alexander the Great, Julius Caesar, and Napoleon—unless they had something to gain by it?" Eddy grasped Jonas by the shoulders. "Has it occurred to you that their contemporaries may have felt and talked about them in much the same way as that choir of mules over in the Capitol talks about Clinton? Only their language was different."

Jonas arose and leaned his elbow against the mantel, staring into the fire. "Somehow I never thought of Clinton that way. Do you really consider him as great as the men you mentioned?"

"Much greater, Jonas. They held the power of death over people. Clinton has only his wits and his two hands. And now please give that bell-pull a yank. I'd like some breakfast before we go to see him."

Two hours later, Jonas Platt and Thomas Eddy found De Witt Clinton in the Senate Chamber. For Platt, Clinton had a casual "How do you do?" For Eddy, in his grey beaver, smartly tailored black suit, polished black boots, and fur-lined coat, he had a warm smile and a hearty handshake. "I remember you very well, Mr. Eddy. I've met you in the City—at the bank and again at political meetings. What can I do for you?"

Eddy offered his cigar case. Clinton took one, lighted it at a nearby candle, removed the cigar from his mouth, nodded at it approvingly, then suggested, "Perhaps we'd better go to the anteroom where we can talk quietly. It's rather noisy here in the Chamber."

Seated in the anteroom, Jonas explained their mission, then handed Clinton the draft of the resolution. Clinton held the scroll in his hand, reflecting for almost a minute before he unrolled it. While reading, he let his cigar go out. After he had finished he chewed the cigar and stroked his chin. There was a faraway look in his eyes.

Eddy started to arise. "Perhaps you'd like some time to think it over, Mr. Clinton?"

Clinton reached out a detaining hand. "No, Mr. Eddy. My mind is made up. I have never given the matter of a canal much thought. Naturally I don't know much about it. But as you have it here," he glanced at the resolution, "it seems to have possibilities. Yes, I'll sponsor this resolution, but first I must ask you to delete the list of names suggested for commissioners."

Clinton explained that some senators like to be on committees and to serve as commissioners partly for the distinction, but mostly for another reason which he described with a wink. Elaborating, he added that naturally they would all vote for a measure requiring the appointing of commissioners because each senator would hope to be one of the appointed. But if the commissioners were named in the resolution, the senators not included in the list would promptly lose interest in the measure and vote against it. The excluded senators being a majority, the bill would be defeated. Suspense was the important factor. Clinton then suggested that Platt offer the measure in the Senate that very morning and promised to second the motion himself.

As Clinton had predicted, when the canal measure was proposed and seconded in the Legislature, the Senators, and afterward the Assemblymen, snapped at the bait of a "Board of Commissioners" to investigate the canal project. Both houses quickly passed the measure with provision for a $3,000 appropriation.

Years afterward, Jones Platt wrote concerning Clinton's sudden interest in the canal. "From that time Mr. Clinton devoted the best powers of his vigorous and capacious mind to this subject. He appeared to grasp and realize it as an object of the highest public utility and worthy of his noblest ambition." Actually, the stimulus which impelled that "vigorous and capacious mind" toward the canal project was the very considerable number of petitions being sent to the Legislature by New York State voters who had suffered from the Jeffersonian embargo.

This economic condition was contemporaneously described as "The Legislature had before them, at that session of 1810, memorials from citizens in different parts of the State representing that Canada was attracting the greater part of our own internal commerce in consequence of the facilities which were afforded by water communications to transport commodities to her market."

Mention of Canada jangled like an alarm bell. Those memorials (petitions) certainly deserved investigation. But the Legislature had not forgotten thrift. It occurred to them that the newly appointed Canal Commissioners could look into the diversion of American commerce to Canada while investigating the practicablility of a canal. All at once a rumor was started—probably by the state senators not chosen as canal commissioners. The rumor was, in effect, a political dirge that having spent many thousands of the taxpayers' hard-earned dollars in developing an almost useless waterway (the Mohawk River and Wood Creek), now the Legislature had appropriated three thousand more to defray the expenses of a group of wealthy men to take a pleasant midsummer jaunt through beautiful central New York. Their ostensible purpose was to investigate the advisability of building another waterway! And, believe it or not, some were taking their wives—all at public expense!

Public reaction to this exaggerated rumor was so emotional that the Commissioners might not have started, but for a new and different petition. The voters in Madison, Oneida, and Onondaga Counties had asked the Legislature to cause the removal of a mud bar which had formed across the outlet of Onondaga Lake. During periods of freshet, when the streams flowing into Onondaga Lake raised the lake level, the mud bar functioned as a dam backing up the excess water and holding it in the lake until the water became saturated by the whitish deposit (supposedly salt) encrusting the lake bottom. Then as the water continued to rise, it overflowed the lake shores and flooded the fields presumably making them salty and unfit for cultivation. Not a word had been said about how the mud bar had blocked the passage of bateaux loaded with casks of salt for the market. And yet a mud bar which had stopped water would naturally also stop a boat. But the bateaumen were not complaining. It therefore seemed to the Legislature that the petitioners in that region must be facetious.

To be certain, the Legislature felt constrained to send out an investigating committee. And since the thrifty Legislature liked killing two birds with one shot, they turned the Onondaga mud bar investigation over to the Commissioners appointed to look into the canal project. To the Legislature the mud bar was of more immediate concern than the canal. Bateaux carrying salt had been coming down the Mohawk River about as usual, and since they all came from Onondaga Lake, the Legislature was interested in knowing, before passing an appropriation, how loaded bateaux managed to get over the mud bar when water could not.

To the Legislature central and western New York rated merely as a turbulent frontier. It was back country with only a scattering of votes. Consequently the Canal Commissioners were not informed about travelling conditions and the overnight accommodations in the region which they were about to explore.

They were soft men, accustomed to luxury and dependent upon the comforts of the city. Their names were De Witt Clinton, Gouverneur Morris, Thomas Eddy, Simeon De Witt, Stephen Van Rensselaer, William North, and Peter B. Porter. Though soft physically, they were able, determined citizens. And appointed in the nick of time, for at the April 15 election for governor, Jonas lost to Daniel Tompkins by a narrow margin. Thenceforth, Jonas would do whatever he could to forward the canal project, but De Witt Clinton must carry the baton. In selecting him Eddy had chosen shrewdly. A fighter rather than a popular man was needed, for Tompkins was just beginning his meteoric rise to power. And Tompkins was fanatically hostile to the canal.

CHAPTER EIGHT

THE CANAL COMMISSIONERS' TOUR OF INVESTIGATION

Four of the appointed commissioners, Thomas Eddy, the secretary and treasurer, Gouverneur Morris, Peter B. Porter, and De Witt Clinton met in New York City in June of 1810 and agreed to forgather at Gregory's Tavern in Albany on July 2 bringing with them their baggage and as many other Commissioners as they could find.

Gouverneur Morris wished to bring along as a consultant a competent surveyor named Latrobe. Immediately Clinton objected, partly because the party would be accompanied by the State Surveyor General, Simeon De Witt, and by surveyor James Geddes, but mostly because Morris wanted to bring Latrobe. Latrobe himself settled the matter by declining because he was too busy.

Morris then informed Clinton that he would bring Mrs. Morris and a landscape painter named Sharpless and that they would not ride in a bateau with the other Commissioners, but would travel in a phaeton drawn by a fine team of horses at Morris' own expense. Clinton's reply was in character. Knowing Morris' extravagant taste in women, he said facetiously that while he had no objection to Mr. Morris travelling by carriage, he hoped that Mrs. Morris would ride in the Commissioners' bateau because her presence would relieve the tedium of a slow journey.

It certainly would have. Mrs. Morris was noted for her sex appeal. But because a portion of feminine allure depends on having beauty aids in place, a woman travelling in summer would require the regrouping facilities of a powder room every two hours. Along the Mohawk river road there might be a tavern or two worthy of her dainty presence. West of the Mohawk River there would be none.

Mrs. Morris made her excuses with smiles and dimples, assuring them that they would find her awaiting at Bagg's Tavern in Utica. And she hoped that they would not be long. Clinton slapped the rump of one of the horses to get the phaeton started. Farewells have to be terminated somehow.

Anticipating the possibility of future political battles over the canal issue, Clinton kept a journal of their trip through western New York to provide statistics for his speeches.

The Commissioners should have left Schenectady in an upriver bateau on July 4. The cause of delay was the neglect of their secretary, Thomas Eddy, to provide in advance for bateaux. Because of that neglect, the principal freight forwarder (and village undertaker), Mr. Walton, had only twenty-four hours' notice. However, he bought for them one bateau, rented another, had both caulked and painted, and had a canopy and curtain rigged amidship on one for the Commissioners and a tarpaulin on the other to protect their baggage. The baggage for each included a travelling bag, small mattress, blanket, and pillow, but regrettably no camp stools and no tent.

These preparations took time. De Witt Clinton, impatient by nature, chafed and stamped at the delay, reminding Eddy every time that he saw him how careless and lazy he had been in forgetting to write ahead and engage the boats. When Eddy was not around Clinton blamed the hot, stuffy little tavern rooms in which they were supposed to sleep, but could not because the rooms were too hot. Also, Clinton found Schenectady distressingly dull. There were a bank, a courthouse, a college, and plenty of trade. The gay crowd which visited Saratoga Springs in the summer also visited

Schenectady, but on that day (the Fourth of July) the gaiety was all in Saratoga.

The Union College students held a Fourth of July parade during the hottest part of the day. The parade ended in a free-for-all fight between the students and the townspeople. The fight which transcended in fury anything seen in the vicinity of Schenectady since the Revolutionary War soothed and quieted Clinton while it lasted, but it was over all too soon. Clinton then resumed his chafing about the dullness of Schenectady and Mr. Walton's incapacity in the matter of finding bateaumen to pole the bateaux up the river.

At 4:00 P.M. on the fourth the paint on the bateaux was not dry, and the caulking had not fully swelled. The bateaumen, aroused from a tavern floor to which they had slipped like four very fiery sunsets, though grave, were far from sober. The river was so low that $50,000 worth of freight had accumulated in the Phinn and Ellice warehouse, waiting to be forwarded upriver. Rain, which would raise the river to a level more suitable for boating, was pending and almost impending. It made no difference. Schenectady was so dull that Clinton could not endure it another minute. So the Commissioners embarked. A crowd gathered at the wharf, waved their hats, cheered, and wished them a pleasant journey. The Commissioners lighted cigars and with considerable satisfaction watched the bateaumen, one at each end of the boat, sweat, puff, and grunt as they jabbed, shoved, and hauled back their eighteen foot iron-tipped poles.

They had rounded Hog Island and were moving slowly about two miles upriver, hugging the south shore bank, when a coarse face crowned by a broken black hat peered over a fringe of bushes along the bank. Then a heavy homemade rake came whizzing down on the boat. No one was hurt, but from the way that the bateaumen, using their poles, vaulted up that bank it looked as though someone might be, and soon. However, the bateaumen were unable to overtake the practical-joking farmhand who had thrown the rake. As a counter joke the bateaumen smashed all of the farmer's haying tools, slid down their poles to the bateaux, and resumed their labors. The Commissioners looked at each other askance. Could this incident foreshadow the type of people they were to find in central New York?

It could. At sundown the bateaumen had poled and strained and cursed the boats through the gaps in the bateau-dam pockets which, due to low water, had become swift, shallow chutes. They were three miles west of Schenectady. The weather was as humid and depressing as ever. From an unpainted shanty on the south bank came drunken shouting and off-key singing. The harsh features of the bateaumen relaxed. One of them confided to Thomas Eddy that they were looking at Willard's, one of the finest taverns along the Mohawk. Without waiting for authorization the bateau-men ran the boats upon the shelving mudbank and hastened to the taproom. The Commissioners, picking up their personal luggage, followed slowly. The close little taproom was crowded with red-faced, glassy-eyed rustics, bawling ballads and cursing.

Among the pig-and-chicken-infested weeds in the yard, a farmer stood on a keg making a Fourth of July speech. The chickens continued their scratching and clucking. Only the pigs appeared to be listening. A burly, coarse-faced tough with a broken black hat, torn shirt, and hairy chest swayed on the porch, partially concealing an advertisement tacked on the wall. He was bellowing that he could lick any man in sight. Clinton gave the broken black hat a glance of recognition, then peered at the poster. But the tough weaved in such a way that he was always between Clinton and the sign. With hands clasped behind his back and head bowed as if in thought, Clinton walked up to him, suddenly lashed out with a hard left hook to the jaw, and as the man collapsed at the edge of the porch floor, Clinton gave him a haymaker with his right that sent him flying. Having cleared the way, Clinton studied the poster. It advertised a power-driven machine for preparing and carding wool and cotton.

Leading the Commissioners, Thomas Eddy walked into the filthy tavern. He immediately walked out again and, followed by the other Commissioners, proceeded briskly down the Schenectady road toward that tavern with the airless little bedrooms. After they had gone, Clinton stepped into the taproom and paused before a Wright's map of the Mohawk River, attached to the wall. The map showed distances, rifts, currents, farms, and place names. The Commissioners had one in their baggage, but Clinton had not bothered to look at it.

Absorbed in thought, Clinton studied the map. He seemed oblivious to the boisterousness which filled the taproom. When one noisy drunk tried to attract Clinton's attention by violently shoving another drunk against him, Clinton administered a return shove which sent both of them sprawling. He continued to concentrate on the map.

Suddenly Clinton turned on them and shouted "Silence!" His tone and the flicker of the candlelight in his hard green eyes wrought a hush. Pointing to the map he demanded, "If you wanted to dig a ditch from here at Little Falls to there at Schenectady, which side of the river would you choose? The north or the south?"

The alcoholic fumes in the yokels' heads seemed to have dissolved from their stupid faces all expression except a little malice and cruelty. Now as their mouths dropped open, while they stared at each other, their faces became totally blank. Clinton repeated his question. Finally a voice mumbled, "South side."

"Why?"

" 'Cause a high rock hill comes right down to the water in two places on the north side."

"Is there any such obstruction on the south bank?"

"Nope."

Turning his back on them, Clinton walked out on the porch and sat down under the poster advertising machinery. Later, when the guests had departed, the tavern proprietor asked Clinton if he wanted supper and a bed, Clinton shook his head. He wanted to be alone. He wanted to think.

Early the next morning, the other Commissioners returned from Schenectady looking as if they had spent the night in hot stuffy rooms. The boats were launched and the tedious journey resumed. While the others chit-chatted Clinton continued in his abstraction.

That night they stopped at Cook's Tavern (Guy Park Manor), where the ceilings were high and sleep possible. The next morning, according to Clinton's journal, they had custard sprinkled with powdered cinnamon for breakfast. When they remarked to the landlady that it did not taste like cinnamon, she replied that it wasn't cinnamon. It was fly specks. That concluded the breakfast. They resumed their journey.

The next day at Kater's rift Thomas Eddy revealed a reflection of his fine Quaker mind. Observing that the Commissioners were hollow-eyed from lack of food and sleep, he sought to divert them by reading aloud from a religious tract written by D. L. Dodge, a New York merchant.

"If a good man does not resist an assailant and submits to be killed, he will go to Heaven. If he kills the assailant, he may send a soul to Hell which if spared might have been converted and saved to life everlasting."

That brought Clinton out of his brown study, but when Eddy explained that authorship of the pamphlet had won for Dodge great admiration among the Quakers, Clinton shrugged and returned to his mood, leaving discussion to the others.

Three days later, on July 9, the Commissioners, convinced that the Mohawk River was no good for bateau travel or anything else for that matter, stepped ashore at Utica Landing. Gouverneur Morris and Stephen Van Rensselaer, looking refreshed and rested and preceded by a strong odor of whiskey, were there to meet them.

De Witt Clinton had reserved rooms for himself and the rest of the bateau party at the Baggs Hotel. Morris and Van Rensselaer had pre-empted them, found them very comfortable, and were eager to thank Clinton for his forethought. Exhausted and depressed, Clinton led his martyred band to a happy-hunting ground for fleas and bedbugs called Bellinger's Tavern.

While the martyrs were futilely trying to find a place in the Bellinger Tavern where the fleas could not find them, Clinton was in the streets seeking facts about the village of Utica. His attention was attracted to a florid, perspiring man, balancing on a rum keg in front of the tavern, making a political speech to loafers, a few bateaumen, some small boys and their dogs about the economic progress of Utica. The orator was Jonas Platt brushing up on his public speaking. Platt was saying that in 1788 Utica had consisted of one house. The more energetic in the audience turned to see that house. Platt quickly added that there were now three hundred houses, four churches, a post office, two newspapers (some of the subscribers could not read), a branch bank of the Manhattan Company with a capital of $100,000, a county clerk, a clerk of the Supreme Court, the Mohawk Turnpike, the Seneca Turnpike, the free road on the south side of the river, and twenty-two lawyers (one lawyer for every seventy-five people).

Clinton interrupted Platt by demanding that he tell the freight rate per hundred pounds from Utica to Albany. Platt instantly recognized Clinton and regarding him reproachfully admitted that it was eight shillings by wagon and six by water. Clinton retorted that it was no wonder that Utica had never amounted to anything and predicted that it never would as long as freight rates ruled so high. Without a word of recognition or even a nod, Clinton capriciously walked away leaving Jonas Platt looking after him with a quizzical smile. Platt knew that it was just De Witt Clinton's idea of humor.

In due course, although reluctantly, the Gouverneur Morris–Van Rensselaer entourage cracked their whips and drove westward at a fast walk. The other Commissioners eased their aching hams down on the hard bateau seats and groaned as the bateaumen gave the boats a vigorous shove upriver. After two miles, during which the Commissioners shifted their weight from right to left and reverse, but without dispelling the illusion that they were developing boils, they appproached the landing of the celebrated Bradbury farm. Having heard that the Commissioners were approaching, Mr. Bradbury in person, stomach bulging with prosperity, was waiting at the landing. As soon as the Commissioners were in sight, Mr. Bradbury welcomed them to his farm. He boomed that he was paying five hundred dollars a year rent, annually made four hundred cheeses, and sold the cheeses together with a number of hogs which fattened on the skimmed milk. He transported his cheeses to the Albany market in his own wagon. His hogs had to walk ahead of the wagon escorted by his dog.

Mr. Eddy remarked that he could not see any hogs. Bradbury yelled. Responding to his call, hogs arose from the mud all over the clearing and grunted a greeting. De Witt Clinton motioned the boatmen on with the comment that he could not distinguish between the farmer and the hogs, and if he should go ashore he might try to shake the wrong hand.

About four miles farther they left the boats in the mouth of Sauquoit Creek and walked up the rutted road to a series of dams flanked by one-story unpainted buildings fitted with tailraces and water wheels. Through opened windows came the rumbling and jolting of six spinning carriages bearing 384 mule-spindles. The water wheels splashed and groaned. The air was heavy with the smell of raw cotton.

The Commissioners poked their heads in at the doors. Practical-minded Thomas Eddy observed that the spinning was the Arkwright system. Clinton, alert to voting possibilities, remarked that the forty employees were all girls and very unhealthy looking girls at that. As there was nothing more to be seen, and as girls, unhealthy or healthy, were not allowed to vote, the Commissioners obeyed the travel urge to hasten and reluctantly returned to the stark realism of the bateau seats.

Their next stop, Rome, a community of seventy houses, a courthouse, church, and state arsenal dotted fairly dry land a few feet above the level of surrounding swamps. The smell testified that the swamps were used as a convenient sewage and waste disposal and as a summer range for hogs. At the tavern they had to listen to unending complaints about Dominick Lynch, a prominent citizen, owner of most of the dry land and much of the swamps, although there was some question about who owned the hogs. Lynch would rent, but would not sell his land. His detractors argued that Lynch's policy was stunting development in Rome and building up Utica. His protagonists insisted that Lynch was a man of vision who was saving Rome for future improvement. When Eddy asked Clinton if future improvement meant more hogs, Clinton growled that anyone with a grain of common sense would know that it meant fewer hogs.

At the tavern the Commissioners also had to listen to Gouverneur Morris, who had lingered partly because he preferred waiting for them there than at the flea-infested hovel about forty miles westward, the first house where they could reunite. A more compelling reason was that his obsession about breaking down the mound of Lake Erie and letting the water flow eastward so that ships could sail directly from the Hudson River to Lake Erie had broken down his own inner restraint. They might have escaped that ordeal if James Geddes had not recently joined the party. The mere sight of James Geddes or Simeon De Witt seemed to bring out the worst in Gouverneur Morris.

The next morning Morris sent his carriage back to New York and ordered his party to board the Geneva stage. Only a vehicle built for it could negotiate a road as primitive as the western turnpike. The other Commissioners descended Wood Creek in their bateaux with a night stop at Gilbert's Tavern on the north side of the Creek. It was a night to remember.

With darkness, swarms of punkies and mosquitos whined from the surrounding swamps and drove the Commissioners inside the tavern. Because of bedbugs infesting the beds the Commissioners lay down on the dirty floor and tried to sleep. People from the surrounding country kept dropping in all night for a mug of home-brew laced with rum. There was cracking of coarse jokes, and pulling and hauling and slapping of the barmaid to make her giggle. When no one flopped on the beds, the bedbugs went hunting for those who should have retired and, when they found them, worked them over. Finally the Commissioners went out, lay on the ground and smoked cigars the rest of the night to drive away the insects.

Not until midmorning and twelve more miles, when the caressing breeze on Oneida Lake took away all of the bugs, did they rest, and then they slept the sleep of exhaustion on those hard bateau seats.

Poling down the outlet of Oneida Lake, the Oneida River, they passed on their left the confluence of the Seneca River known then as Three Rivers. Two miles below, the Oswego River was choked for hundreds of yards by lumber rafts unable to pass a rock-toothed rift because of low water. The bateaumen held a bitterly profane interchange with the raftmen which resulted in a way being opened between the logs to let the bateaux pass.

Out from the shore came a string of half-laden salt boats following the bateaux. From tense voices the Commissioners learned that the rafts were bound for Quebec but had been stranded for four weeks. The raftmen were so disgruntled that they had refused to make the slightest effort to open a way for the salt boats which were bound for American ports on Lake Erie.

So redoubtable was the fighting reputation of the bateaumen that it had proved to be unnecessary for them to demolish the raftmen to gain passage. Impressed by the bateaumen's fierce scowls the raftmen even agreed to keep the passage open long enough to permit the salt boats to return and take the rest of their loads down the swift shallow rapids.

While huge aromatic hemlock and pine logs were being pushed aside for the bateaux, De Witt Clinton asked Thomas Eddy to appraise the dollar value of the rafts. Eddy stood up and counted logs for a while, then said that if the raftmen would guarantee to deliver the rafts intact at Quebec, he would pay on delivery $20,000 a raft. Eddy added that he could not understand attempting to float logs such a distance when Adirondack pine and hemlock cut and floated down the Saranac River could so much more easily be rafted at the mouth and poled down Lake Champlain and the Sorel River to the St. Lawrence River and Quebec. He added that because a hemlock raft would become waterlogged and sink after a few months, the arrival of the hemlock at Quebec was highly doubtful and that it was a pity that the State of New York could provide no better means of transportation than the hazards of the Oswego River and windy Lake Ontario. After all, why should the products of New York find a seaport at Quebec instead of New York harbor?

While Eddy could not find an answer to his own questions he had succeeded in intriguing the interest of the other Commissioners. At the short carry around the falls of the Oswego, the Commissioners learned from a portage teamster that annually 15,000 bushels of salt passed that carry, much of which was sold to the Canadians, and that 15,000 bushels had gone over the carry that summer. More was to follow, indicating that New York commerce with Canada was growing. The only hopeful note was that a saw-and-gristmill to utilize the waterpower was being built across the carry by Joshua Forman. When completed, this industrial development would obstruct commerce on the Oswego River sufficiently to cause shippers to seek another route.

Having floated into Oswego, the Commissioners came face to face with some facts about the salt trade which showed how dangerously far American commerce had drifted toward Canada. They had heard it rumored in New York but had never visualized it as a reality. Having seen the lumber rafts and salt bateaux, they could understand and appreciate the statistics which they were about to find. Port records showed that 19,000 barrels of salt had been shipped from Oswego in 1808, and that 3,000 barrels of salt had been left in storage that year for lack of shipping space. In 1809, 29,000 barrels of salt had been shipped to Canada. Two-thirds of that salt had been transported by the Canadians across Lake Ontario and Lake Erie and sold to Americans in the state of Ohio. The price of a barrel of salt at Salina on Lake Onondaga was two dollars, at Kingston, Ontario four and a half dollars, at Pittsburgh, Pennsylvania it was eight and a half dollars. The bateau freight rate on salt from Salina to Oswego during normal water level was four shillings per bushel. During low water it was six. Thomas Eddy estimated that the rate for salt on a dug canal from

Salina to Albany, if there were such a canal, would be three shillings per bushel. The Commissioners puffed their cigars and became quiet and thoughtful.

The return to Three Rivers because of long, dangerous rapids below Oswego Falls required the bateaumen to drag the bateaux up the river by tumpline. To ease that burden, the Commissioners, each carrying his own baggage, walked toward Three Rivers expecting to arrive well ahead of the bateaumen. There were so many outcropping stones and washouts in the road that the Commissioners found it expedient to walk in single file. This order of march, though unsociable, was conducive to pondering upon transportation costs and the rapidly increasing drift of upper New York State commerce toward Canada. Because the road, though roughly paralleling the river, was set back at some distance from it, the Commissioners lost track of the bateaumen.

The Commissioners spent that night sleeping on the floor at Van Valkenburgh's Tavern. A frost so heavy that it destroyed most of the growing corn in central New York chilled the Commissioners until they wondered whether upon arriving at the tavern they had been prudent in declining the featherbed which Van Valkenburgh had offered. They knew all about tavern featherbeds and the dividends that went with them. By 3:00 A.M., sleep being out of the question, they arose and stamped around the taproom until Van Valkenburgh appeared with a lantern. They hung their baggage on him, took his lantern, and started up the road toward the falls.

At the falls, Van Valkenburgh, with their baggage draped by ropes from his shoulders, overtook them. For his services as porter he overcharged them four shillings. When Thomas Eddy objected, Van Valkenburgh angrily exclaimed, "What odds does it make to you? The State pays for it."

There was a dramatic silence while in the glimmering of dawn, pale haggard faces registered horror. Then in cold, measured tones Thomas Eddy expounded to Van Valkenburgh the iniquity of frivolous disbursement of the taxpayer's money.

Before Eddy had finished, Van Valkenburgh was insulting them collectively and individually. Van Valkenburgh was a powerful man, but so was De Witt Clinton, and by that time Clinton was wearing his "fighting face" and inching toward Van Valkenburgh with measuring eye and doubled fists. The light was so dim that Van Valkenburgh, moving with the agility of a backwoodsman, could have licked all of the other Commissioners singlehanded and then exacted his tip. However, there was enough light so that Van Valkenburgh could also see that an Irish fight was coming his way. With a valedictory that he hoped never again to carry so many bags so many miles at three o'clock on a frosty morning for such sanctimonious gentlemen without a fifty-cent tip, Van Valkenburgh turned and vanished into the cold mist.

A few hours later, when the Commissioners stumbled into a tavern at the upper falls of the Oswego, they found their bateaumen waiting. It was at this tavern, rather than at Van Valkenburgh's, that the bateaumen had expected them to hole up. Upon arrival the preceding evening, the bateaumen had found a country dance in full swing. Appreciating the courtesy of the Commissioners in walking and carrying their baggage to make poling against a strong current easier for them, the bateaumen had resolved to get the tavern quieted down so that when the tired Commissioners arrived they would be able to sleep. The method chosen by the bateaumen typified the ingenuity and the brutality of their social level. They had chopped the tail off a casual dog, turned the dog loose in the crowded dance hall and closed the door. The blood squirting from the stump of the dog's tail had spattered the women's dresses so extensively that amid pretty little screams and shrieks the women had departed all at one time. After the women and the dog had gone and things had stopped falling, a deep silence had pervaded the tavern. Unfortunately, the Commissioners had not arrived in time to enjoy it.

The family operating the tavern at Three Rivers was not on hand to greet the Commissioners the next day when their bateaux slushed up on the black mud beach. The family had been laid low by dysentery. In fact, they were all the way down. This was the filthy hovel from which the Commissioners had been driven by victorious bedbugs a few nights previously. On that occasion Thomas Eddy, thinking to turn an honest penny, had bet the maid of all work a dollar that she would not have the tavern cleaned by the time of their return. When they walked in, Eddy took a good look around and then with pretended cheerfulness parted with a silver dollar.

Poling up the narrow, placid Seneca River, the Commissioners passed the outlet of Onondaga Lake without pausing. They assured each other that on their return trip they would investigate Salina, the famous salt works at the opposite side of the lake. As for the mysterious mud bar in the outlet which had sparked their expedition, they were encountering too many obstacles of their own to give it any attention. Probably they had forgotten all about it.

Farther up the Seneca River they stopped at Seneca Falls to inspect Mynderse's gristmill, producer of the finest flour in the country. Because of its quality, Mynderse flour had for some time commanded a premium of four shillings a barrel in the New York market. The miller offered the simple explanation that all of the Mynderse flour was ground from wheat raised in the Genesee Valley.

The Genesee Valley was long and wide. Hundreds of farms would be required to extract the Genesee Valley's full potential of wheat. Several dozens of gristmills would scarcely have sufficed to grind it. Unquestionably, enough excellent flour could be produced to feed everyone in New York State and provide a large surplus for export besides.

The miller added that the same thing could be said of the salt produced a few miles eastward at Salina. There was no limit to the wealth of extractive produce which could be shipped from central New York—if there were an inexpensive way of transporting it.

The Commissioners exchanged significant glances. Most of them had spent their lives in New York City or the Hudson Valley. A potential of wealth like that of the Genesee Valley had never occurred to them. The miller, reading their expressions, smiled and said that if they thought that the amount of grain which might be produced in the Genesee Valley sounded like a lot, they should visit the rolling plains between the Ohio River and Lake Erie. The quantity of grain which could be raised in that region was incalculable. Already people in central New York were abandoning farms hardly wrested from the wilderness and thronging the western turnpikes. Many men would be needed to settle the Ohio country, but a goodly number were on their way. They would make a trail which others could follow.

When the Commissioners urged the question of transportation of Ohio grain, the miller seemed a bit astonished. He assured them that Canadian sloops sailing from Lake Erie into the mouths of the Cuyahoga and Maumee Rivers would transport all of the grain offered for shipment and all of the casks of Kentucky tobacco and whiskey (presently routed through Montreal to New York), just as they had been for the past ten years.

When the Commissioners appeared incredulous, the miller suggested that they visit the mouth of the Cuyahoga River and see for themselves. At Seneca Falls the Commissioners were approximately three hundred and twenty-five trail miles from the confluence of the Cuyahoga River with Lake Erie. Under existing travel conditions it seemed like three thousand. Naturally, the Commissioners were willing to take the miller's word for it.

At Seneca Falls the Commissioners had already passed the Montezeuma, one of the big New York State swamps. They were to pass several more. All of these swamps were infested with anopheles mosquitoes, carriers of malaria, locally called swamp fever. Unaware of the functioning and, indeed, of the existence of the deadly anopheles, they attributed the cause of the fever to the swamp mists and emanations from the stagnant water. To avoid the emanations the Commissioners stayed indoors after sundown which, of course, shut out the mosquitoes and the fever. Meanwhile they dosed themselves with medicines prescribed for the occasion by Dr. Hosack. In his journal De Witt Clinton mentioned James Fever Powders, Elixir Proprietalis, Bark and Emetic, Lee's Anti-bilious Pills made of calomel and gamboge with a soap binder. Not included in the list of medicines, but casually mentioned elsewhere, was their actual defense against malaria—several hundred cigars. The nicotine in cigar smoke is poison gas to all mosquitoes. The Commissioners whiled away the tedious hours by telling funny stories, playing the flute, singing, and smoking cigars. When not eating or sleeping they were smoking.

At Geneva on Seneca Lake, the head of navigation, they sold their bateaux, paid off the bateaumen, and continued their journey westward by stage. When they arrived at Irondequot Landing they put up at Serren's Tavern. The number of noisy drunks in attendance was almost normal, but the concentration of fleas was fantastic. The Commissioners suffered, but they did not neglect their investigations. They learned that from Irondequot Bay white fish were being taken, salted, barreled, and shipped to Charlottesburg at the confluence of the Genesee River and Lake Ontario. From Charlottesburg they were shipped at $12.00 per barrel to Canada. The Commissioners also learned that during that summer shipments to Canada from Charlottesburg had included 1,000 barrels each of flour, pork, and potash, and upwards of 100,000 staves.

Numbed with fatigue and shaky from lack of proper nourishment, the Commissioners jolted on in the Batavia stage. They stopped at Sibley's Tavern twenty-five miles west of Batavia. In their depressed condition, of first importance was the discovery that at that tavern there were no drunks or fleas of any consequence; of secondary importance was the information that nine miles southwest of the Tavern could be found a group of salt-spring works producing mainly for the vicinity.

The salt works were capable of a much larger production, but adjacent roads were primitive. There was no water transportation. It was another instance of undeveloped natural wealth. The Commissioners inquired further. Suppose someone should build a serviceable road from the salt works to Lake Erie, only nine miles westward, would not the Canadian lake schooners pick up and pay cash for all of that salt? The tavern-keeper replied that the Canadians would.

In conversations with the natives at the bar of Sibley's Tavern the Commissioners became disagreeably aware of a faltering devotion not only to the Federal Government, which to these people was rather remote, but even to the State Government. Here at the western extremity of New York State the people had the privilege of paying taxes and of voting for someone whom they did not know and had hardly seen. They felt isolated—cut off. They did their business mostly with Canadians.

The Commissioners lighted fresh cigars and again talked it over among themselves. It was well that they lighted those cigars for beyond Ellicott, the next settlement, they saw a man languishing with fever. At Stuart's Tavern in Niagara County another man was sick with fever. In both instances they left some medicine and pushed on. That night, alarmed by fancied danger of contagion from the sick man in the tavern, they (including Mrs. Morris) slept as a group on the ground under one large piece of sail cloth—all the way under. The mosquitoes could not get at them.

Bumping along in any conveyance they could hire, they travelled northwestward to Lewiston, the Lake Ontario end of the thirty-mile portage around Niagara Falls to Lake Erie. The Commissioners learned, after arriving at Lewiston that Porter, Barton & Co. had leased the portage from New York State and that they were doing nothing to improve the road which from years of use had worn into deep ruts and pitchholes. For transportation on that road, three yokes of oxen were hitched to each of seven wagons. During the season of lake navigation each wagon, loading twelve barrels of salt, creaked and groaned from Lewiston to Lake Erie between sunrise and sunset. The next day the wagons returned, usually empty. Fifty years previously teams of horses had hauled similar wagons loaded with bales of furs eastward, returning westward more or less empty. The value and nature of the freight had changed, and the direction. Otherwise the road was as backward as the people who plied it.

However, a few small communities of enterprising people had sprung up. There was one at Niagara Falls where a rudimentary manufacturer operated a carding machine which prepared wool for home spinning wheels. A water wheel, powered by water in a tubular chute made of hollowed logs, turned the machine. The wheel also turned a sawmill, a gristmill, and a mill which ground bark for a tannery. Another manufacturer bought hemp from the Genesee Valley at $280 per ton and paid another $100 per ton to transport it to Niagara Falls. He bought tar in New York City and brought it in at a cost of $9 per hundred weight. He had built a rope walk and was supplying rope to nearly all of the ships on the Great Lakes. There was a post office, a tavern, and a few houses. Segregated from commercial centers, the people of Niagara Falls had gone about as far industrially as they could. With the low-cost transportation of a canal they could profitably expand their rope-walk business and ship rope in quantity to the Atlantic seaboard.

At Niagara Falls the Commissioners also learned that across the Niagara River in the Canadian village of Chippewa there was the Stevens Inn, where fleas and bedbugs were reportedly nonexistent, the beds clean and comfortable, and the food excellent. Mrs. Gouverneur Morris, who had taken her husband for better or worse and had experienced the worse, if not the worst, that night when they all slept together on the ground under a sail cloth, persuaded her husband that it was not only inconvenient but unlucky to sleep thirteen in a bed. Something should be done to break the evil spell. The other Commissioners being of the same mind, they ferried across the Niagara River and registered at the Stevens Inn.

While most of the Commissioners were investigating the commerce of Chippewa, Mr. and Mrs. Morris were trying to persuade the innkeeper to let them have the bridal suite, so-called because it was a large airy bedroom with an alcove bedroom. The innkeeper demurred because Lt. Governor Jackson, representative of the Crown in Upper Canada, had sent a special messenger ahead to reserve the room for that day and was hourly expected.

Urged by a baleful glitter in the eyes of Mrs. Morris, Gouverneur Morris crossed and recrossed the innkeeper's palm with silver so many times that the innkeeper gave him the alcove bedroom. Knowing that the alcove could be reached only by passing through the main bedroom, Mrs. Morris gave her husband a nod which implied "I'll take it from here."

When Governor Jackson arrived and found that Mr. and Mrs. Morris were in residence in the alcove he turned upon them a blast of true British profanity and insolence. At that point Mrs. Morris who had been around enough to know what the Governor's cusswords meant, took a hand. When she had finished talking, the Governor was no longer listening. He was on his way down the street looking for other lodgings. He found them not at an inn, but at a tavern where bedbugs were existent—definitely.

Meanwhile the other Commissioners had found in a Chippewa store some excellent wine glasses, jelly glasses, and window glass, all manufactured in Pittsburgh, Pennsylvania and shipped to Canada. The glass had been transported in bateaux, possibly with other articles made in Pittsburgh, down the Ohio River to the confluence of the Muskingum; up the Muskingum to the headwaters portage, and down the Cuyahoga River to Lake Erie and a Canadian schooner which carried them to Fort Erie, a Canadian port. From Erie the glass was hauled by wagon to Chippewa. Significantly the glass could have been carried farther on that same road to Newark, a Canadian port on Lake Ontario. From Newark there was, in summer, water transportation to the Canadian seaport, Montreal. And as western Pennsylvania, Ohio, and Kentucky developed industrially that would be the route by which the products of those states would find a market—unless a canal were built from Lake Erie to the Hudson River.

On August 3 the Commissioners held a formal meeting at the Stevens Inn. It was resolved that as it was not necessary for them to travel farther westward, they would disband and, not as a group, but as individuals, return home. Their next meeting would be at the City Hotel in New York City.

James Geddes recrossed the Niagara River to investigate the Tonawanda Creek and the low hills north of that Creek. The rest of the Commissioners proceeded through well cultivated country to New Amsterdam (Buffalo), passing a factory making red earthenware at Black Rock, New York.

At New Amsterdam, built by the Holland Land Company, a settlement of forty houses, five lawyers, and no church, they hired two carriages and a baggage wagon, bid farewell to one of the Commissioners, Colonel Porter, and started for Albany.

De Witt Clinton's journal mentions sawmills and grist-mills along the way. He also noted that there were peddlers from Connecticut all over the Genesee country selling wooden clocks for twenty dollars apiece and bartering tinware for feathers.

The Seneca Turnpike had been built as far west as Canandaigua. As the Commissioners "rocked and rolled" on that comparatively smooth forest road, they found themselves in "a great concourse of travellers." Considering the sparsely settled country, it must have seemed as if some magic had called such a throng out of the woods. There were a few extensive clearings. In two such openings they saw nurseries of peach trees and apple trees.

From Geneva on Seneca Lake a state road sliced south-westward between Seneca Lake and Crooked Lake to Bath. The road was not much, but the Commissioners followed it because at Bath it connected with the Susquehannah and Bath turnpike which ran eastward through Ithaca and eventually descended into the Hudson Valley at Newburgh. The Commissioners had heard along the way that Ithaca was becoming a trading center. Naturally they wished to see it.

Approaching Ithaca from Bath, the Commissioners were impressed by the extent of the clearings and the prosperous appearance of the crops, and pastures dotted with merino sheep. On roadside trees there were signs advertising carding machinery.

In Ithaca there was a tannery. For this flourishing agriculture and nascent industry the turnpike was obviously responsible. Hides and merino wool in the New York market fetched such high prices that they could be transported by wagons over the expensive turnpike route to the Hudson River and transshipped by steamboat to New York.

Furthermore the people in Ithaca were energetic and purposeful. They talked of clearing more land for grazing and for raising wheat. They were shipping flour by boat the length of Cayuga Lake, through the outlet to Seneca River, the Oswego River and Oswego. Canadian boats took the flour from Oswego to Montreal, their most certain market.

During the winter the Ithacans hauled sleighloads of barreled flour by turnpike about twenty-five miles southward to Owego on the Susquehannah. At Owego they cut logs, sawed them into planks, pegged the planks together into crude boats called arks, loaded the barreled flour into the arks, and in the spring steered them down the Susquehannah to Baltimore, where they sold the flour, as well as the arks (for lumber), and boarded a coast-wise vessel for New York. With the proceeds of the flour and the lumber they bought goods in New York which were scarce in Ithaca and transferred them to Albany by boat and to Ithaca by freight wagon.

The preceding spring they had augmented their shipment of flour with two thousand barrels of salt beef and pork. Ithaca was making money. That was the kind of community De Witt Clinton liked to see. Nevertheless, one thing worried Clinton and the other Commissioners as well. The merchants of Ithaca could ship to Baltimore only while the Susquehannah was in spring freshet, and that lasted for only two or three weeks each year. They could ship by freight wagon over turnpikes to Newburgh and Albany, but wagon transportation was expensive. Actually, most of the shipments from Ithaca went to Montreal because that route was cheaper and more convenient. On the whole, it was disturbing to think that Canada was absorbing New

York State commerce almost down to the Pennsylvania border.

It was time for the Commissioners to move along. On the map Ithaca was a hub for five roads like spokes. To return to the Seneca Turnpike the Commissioners chose a state road which cut eastward through the forest and connected with the road running north along the east bank of Cayuga Lake and the military road. Two left turns in forty bumpy miles brought them to Auburn, which derived its name from Goldsmith's "Deserted Village."

Auburn was not deserted. It had tanneries, distilleries, potasheries, wagon-makers, chair-makers, saddlers, tailors, taverns, blacksmiths, doctors, and a library. Approaching Auburn beside the fourteen mile outlet of Owasco Lake, Clinton counted nine sawmills besides carding machines, turners' shops, a trip-hammer, oil mills, gristmills, fulling mills, a bark mill, and one furnace for melting old iron. On the Seneca Turnpike, which passed through Auburn, the Commissioners saw droves of sheep bleating protests as sheep dogs nipped them toward the New York market.

Rolling eastward, the Commissioners passed Salina close to Onondaga Lake. Clinton noted that the annual output of the salt works was two hundred and sixty thousand bushels. Nearby there was a furniture factory. East of Salina, with the end of the trip in sight, they found the taverns cleaner and better (meaning fewer fleas) and the farms more prosperous. More land had been cleared. Clinton did not take the time to investigate whether it had been cleared to compensate for the acres made sterile by the overflow caused by the mud bar in Onondaga Lake outlet. Like the other Commissioners, Clinton was in a hurry to get home.

Approaching Herkimer, the Commissioners passed an Indian encampment. The Indians were busy binding brooms and weaving baskets for the market. While the Commissioners were preoccupied with watching Indians "at work," a chartered stage filled with young Southerners drove up. The Southerners said that they had heard of the developing industry in New York State and had travelled hundreds of miles to see it.

Thomas Eddy looked at De Witt Clinton. Clinton looked at the Indians. The Indians concentrated on their baskets. In Clinton's mind opportunity was knocking, a small opportunity, but not one to be ignored.

Climbing out of the carriage Clinton addressed the young Southerners with fervor. He said that they, the Commissioners, were completing an extensive tour of the villages of central and western New York. Some villages were failing, others prospering. By making comparisons they had concluded that "although there seems to be in New York a mania for erecting villages, such establishments cannot prosper unless predicated on manufactures. A nascent spirit of industry is burgeoning in this land. Even the Indians, gentlemen—even the Indians."

CHAPTER NINE

THE WASHINGTON SIDE STEP

After returning to their homes the Commissioners were somewhat in the position of gardeners who must first plant seeds, then cultivate the growing shoots before they can harvest. First of all, their friends and neighbors had to hear all about the trip. The seed which the Commissioners planted was naturally somewhat oversize. As the stories spread to friends and friends of friends, the shoots were cultivated until they had grown almost beyond recognition.

By March 2, 1811 it was time for the harvest. The stories of the Commissioners' trip had become so exaggerated that people were beginning to wonder just what they had found. Therefore, on that March day, Gouverneur Morris appeared before the State Senate to read the report of the Canal Commissioners; a statement which accurately set forth the condition of the economy in central and western New York. After the reading Mr. Morris would of course answer questions. Good publicity had been gained by delaying the report until public curiosity had reached a peak. Morris had been chosen as spokesman, partly for his prestige and partly because of his resonant voice.

Jonas Platt was among the listening senators. The narrowness of the margin by which Platt had lost the gubernatorial election had not helped Tompkins, but it had made of Platt an important public figure. Platt was now in a position to support Clinton if Clinton should make a main issue of the canal. It had been Platt's hope that the public reading of this report and the consequent wrangle would start a political battle from which Clinton would emerge as the logical candidate of a large faction of insurgent Republicans in the 1813 gubernatorial election. With "A Dug Canal" as their slogan Platt was sure that he could back Clinton with a large number of Federalist votes—perhaps enough to turn the tide.

Morris put a few senators to sleep with a description of the topography of western New York. He lulled several others by describing the need and practicability of a canal. Still others were looking right at him without seeing him while he ruled out as fallacious all thoughts of a route which included navigation over any part of Lake Ontario.

Then that "Break Down the Mound of Lake Erie" obsession mounted a fanatical look in his eye. He did not go so far as to describe how ships could sail from the Hudson River to Lake Erie, but he did say that the canal should be an inclined plane from Lake Erie to the ridge between Schenectady and Albany with a uniform slope of six inches to the mile.

The snores stopped. The Senate Chamber became suddenly very quiet. The Senators looked at each other questioningly. Followed a buzzing of whispers. A voice, speaking out of order, ignored the Senate President's gavel and demanded to be told how an inclined plane could cross the four miles of bottomless swamp at the Lake Cayuga outlet, or the deep valley of the swift Schoharie. With a nod to the President, Morris acknowledged the question and replied that the canal would be carried over the big swamp on an embankment one hundred and thirty feet high. He added that the Schoharie could be passed on an embankment one hundred and fifty feet high.

Unbelief darkened the senatorial brows as they turned to each other askance. Would not there have to be an almost continuous embankment varying in height according to the hills and valleys most of the distance between Lake Erie and Schenectady? As the obvious answer dawned on them their reaction was another shocked silence. Then they broke into a roar of laughter.

Jonas Platt and De Witt Clinton exchanged glances across the Chamber. Both understood that ridicule of the entire canal project would follow such derisive laughter. The canal, far from becoming a reality, would continue a byword and a joke.

Unperturbed, Morris continued reading his report. He declared that the Commissioners would protest any attempt by an individual or a company to build the canal, because if successful they might increase the lock fees to make their investment lucrative, and there would be an end to cheap transportation. Morris concluded with a construction cost estimate of five million dollars. Then as an afterthought he added, "Experience has long since exploded in Europe the idea of using the beds of rivers for internal navigation."

The reference to European canals added to the report a fillip in keeping with the Morris reputation.

At the close of the day's session De Witt Clinton, Stephen Van Rensselaer, Peter Porter and Jonas Platt held a secret conference on how best to muzzle Gouverneur Morris and his "incline plane" idea. They agreed that his overpowering manner, his wealth, and strong political position in both Albany and Washington made him a valuable asset to the canal project, but that his chimerical schemes for building the canal were giving the State Legislature the best laugh it had had in years. After explosive recriminations they agreed that although Morris should have his head ducked in a pail, tolerance at that moment would be more intelligent. If the cost of building the canal were indeed to be five million, the resources of the Federal Government would have to be invoked. The State of New York just did not have that kind of money. And Morris could be very helpful in getting a canal act passed through Congress. They further reasoned that under proper sponsorship a canal act might meet with less petulance in Congress (which had not had much experience with canals) than in the State Legislature (which had).

As a result of that secret conference a "buck passing" act was approved by the State Legislature on April 8, reappointing the Canal Commissioners and adding the names of Robert Fulton and ex-Chancellor Livingston to the list. The act also authorized the Commissioners:

"To make application on behalf of New York State to Congress or to the Legislature of any state to cooperate or aid in the undertaking of building the canal and to the proprietors of land through which the canal would pass for cessions or grants of land.

"To learn on what terms the Lock Navigation Company would surrender their rights to the State.

"To employ surveyors and engineers.

"To have an appropriation of $15,000 for expenses."

The immediate benefit of the act was to put De Witt Clinton back into circulation. Daniel Tompkins had pushed him off the front page. Robert Williams had pushed Clinton into the street. But Clinton's pioneer work in exploring for a canal restored him to prominence as a topic of polite conversation.

At a Republican caucus of April 1811 to nominate a successor to the late Lieutenant Governor John Broome, Clinton was chosen. The Tammany Society convoked by Teunis Wortman, formerly one of Clinton's best friends, and presided over by Mangle Minthorne, the father-in-law of Governor Tompkins, held an overflow meeting in Martling's beer hall to protest Clinton's nomination because he had opposed the election of Madison for president.

Nettled by the resolutions of the Tammany meeting, Clinton persuaded some of his friends to hold a counterblast meeting of the Citizens of New York at the Union Hotel. Included among the "Citizens" were many immigrant Irish who at that time were not considered sufficiently civilized to belong to Tammany.

At the Union Hotel meeting the Irish were in good attendance, partly in support of their fellow Irishman and benefactor, De Witt Clinton, and partly because of the free drinks. The Tammany Society, in token of their disagreement, barged in on the Citizens' Meeting and started pulling and hauling and clobbering with canes. Instead of being dismayed by this type of social recognition, the Irish were entranced. Indeed, they acquitted themselves very well.

When the meeting was over, no one had changed his opinion of De Witt Clinton. His detractors maintained that Clinton was trying to establish "a pernicious family aristocracy under which devotion to his person would be the exclusive test of merit and the only passport to promotion." His protagonists insisted that, unlike Tammany which had its back to the future, Clinton was looking ahead.

For the Federalists who had been fighting shoulder to shoulder with the Irish, blacked eyes were so numerous as to be almost a badge of party. A few days later, when Tammany made overtures to the Federalists about a fusion in the approaching election, the Federalists just could not see it. In consequence the Federalists nominated their own candidate, Nicholas Fish. In New York City, Fish polled over 2,000 votes. Clinton, the Republican candidate, and Willett, the Tammany candidate, received six or seven hundred votes each. But in the state-wide election, Clinton, because of his interest in a canal became the champion of the upstate voters. They made him Lieutenant Governor by a large plurality.

The Republican caucus which nominated Clinton was the last one. After that, candidates were chosen at county conventions.

His election to the office of Lieutenant Governor restored De Witt Clinton's self-assurance and moroseness. To genial

Gouverneur Morris, Clinton's churlishness was a challenge. For most of Clinton's sarcastic replies and caustic comments Morris had a humorous interpretation. Since Morris enjoyed laughing at his own jokes, he found in Clinton a source of uproarious mirth which failed only when Clinton, infected by the Morris brand of humor, began to laugh in spite of himself and thus became temporarily agreeable.

One topic which provoked no levity in Morris was the canal. In his own estimation he had been father and mother to it and had reared it to teen-age. Blocking the way to its maturity were three hard questions. Who would advance the estimated cost of five million dollars? And if the money should be forthcoming, who would have sufficient knowledge of canal construction and the skill to build a canal through three hundred and fifty miles of wilderness? Assuming that the first two questions might be answered, and the canal built, would there be enough traffic to yield lock fees sufficient to meet the cost of maintenance and amortization of debt?

Discussing these three questions after the convocation of the State Legislature in January of 1812, Morris and Clinton arrived concurrently at what seemed the obvious solution—pass the buck to the Federal Government at Washington.

Of course, someone had to do the passing. Those Canal Commissioners who were available, with the approval of the leaders in the Legislature, composed a letter to President Madison and another to Congress urging the cooperation of the Federal Government in financing the construction of a canal from Lake Erie to the Hudson River. Because of his many contacts in Congress, Morris was deputized to convey the letters. Clinton was asked to accompany him because of his firsthand knowledge of the topography of the canal route and because his uncle George, the ex-governor, had for several years been vice-president of the United States. They would travel in open sleighs in midwinter.

Although Morris and Clinton, as deputies, seemed the obvious choice, the Canal Commissioners could hardly have chosen two men less qualified to promote Federal backing for a New York State canal. President Madison, to whom they must first present their protocol, was a friend of the Tammany Society. Tammany was hostile to both Morris and Clinton.

Judging President Madison by themselves, the Commissioners reasoned that he would be flattered at having two such important figures as Clinton and Morris appear before him as suppliants. He might have, at that, if they had been suppliant. Instead, upon their arrival in Washington they comported themselves like big shots and from that elevated plane, sounded off to several Congressmen on the subject of the canal. They later reported the unfavorable response of those Congressmen to their advances as due to "a feeling of jealousy against New York State among the members of Congress."

The Congressmen of that time were mostly farmers and lawyers. Their circumstances were modest and their salaries meager. Therefore, it was no problem for Clinton, a wealthy man, and Morris, one of the very wealthy, to impress by their ostentation such insignificant men. But the reaction of the Congressmen was not to bow the knee; rather to draw the knife. Clinton and Morris saw that they had used a wrong approach, and that if they pushed on and made a direct request for an appropriation, they would be walking into an ambush which would cost them a loss of dignity. Instead, it seemed more intelligent to use Uncle George Clinton as a stalking horse for a furtive advance upon wily President Madison.

The President received them with a show of cordiality, listened to their story with an air of approval and said that he would be glad to send a message to Congress commending consideration of a canal appropriation. Thus the dignity of Clinton and Morris, and perhaps New York State, was saved. But nothing tangible was accomplished.

Because Morris and Clinton were prominent men, Congress saluted them with a spectacular side step rather than a polite brush-off. After Congress had heard and applauded the President's message, the Speaker of the House introduced Morris as the man "who had contributed to the Constitution of the United States its lucidity of phrase and clearness and exactness of language." He then asked Morris to present his case to the Representatives. Morris needed no introduction. Those who did not know him would never forget the hearty, interesting speech he made about the importance of a canal in joining the West to the East, like tying the country together.

After the ovation which followed, the Speaker looked at Clinton over his glasses, hesitated a moment as if waiting for Clinton to add something, then cleared his throat and referred the matter to a large committee.

This Committee, with a show of enthusiasm, then drafted a canal bill on a basis of canals not only for New York, but for several states. In the bill, grants of government lands provided for the cost of construction. No tolls would be charged above the amounts necessary to keep the canals in repair.

The committee drafted and redrafted the bill until the eve of Morris' and Clinton's departure for New York. Then they reported the bill favorably. Believing that they had won their point and that because of the size of the committee the bill was as good as passed, Clinton and Morris took off for New York without waiting for the actual vote and passage of the bill. Scarcely had the jingling of their sleigh bells died away when the committee, for superficial reasons, reversed its decision and buried the bill. Within hours the Representatives had forgotten about the canal and resumed their usual squabbling about matters which to them seemed important.

Although Morris and Clinton knew about the tactic of side step and in their pasts had used it themselves, it had not occurred to them that in spite of Uncle George, Congress would side step them. So confident were they that they had indeed persuaded Congress and the President to underwrite the constructing of a New York State canal that they began anticipating some of the questions which might be asked by Congress later.

Obviously, the Federal Government could not build the canal without first acquiring the franchise of the Lock Navigation Company. Therefore, after a conference, the Canal Commissioners requested the holders of all of the shares in the Lock Navigation Company, excluding those held by the State, to disclose the price at which they would sell their holdings. Because of the publicity which Clinton and Morris had given their fancied triumph in Washington the shareholders, knowing that the Federal Government would be their prospective customer, set the price for their worthless stock at $190,000.

This was the first shock to Clinton and Morris. The second came when, after several months of silence, it became quite apparent that Congress had no intention of doing anything about a New York State canal. The true and obvious reason (though for Clinton the most obscure) was that Congress, having but little money to appropriate, had been saying "No" to nearly all requests for unusual expenditures. Seeking less obvious explanation for failure, Clinton blamed the fabulous cost of the Morris plan, an inclined plane from Lake Erie to the Hudson. Resolved not to be an apologist for Morris, Clinton developed his theory, footnoting that while Morris had been back-slapping reluctant Congressmen, Clinton had talked with some of the foreign ambassadors residing in Washington about the credit of New York State aboard. To his secret astonishment, Clinton had learned that New York, on its own unendorsed credit, could borrow from Europe for a paltry 6 percent per annum, five million dollars to be repaid within fifteen years. Under these circumstances Clinton could see no reason why the State of New York should not let go of the hand of her Federal parent, and Morris and his inclined plane also, and build her own canal!

Consequently, when the Canal Commissioners submitted to the Legislature a canal plan, they included an inclined plane only from Lake Erie to Seneca Outlet. The rest of the way the boats would progress by means of locks. This plan was quite as unworkable as the inclined plane for the entire route, but it signified that Morris had lost enough prestige through his fiasco in Washington to encourage the other Commissioners to stand up to him until a complete change of plan could be effected.

When the snow had melted into the summer of 1811, James Geddes and Benjamin Wright* made a joint survey of the canal route. After their report had been made public, popular sentiment for a workable canal became so strong that Morris withdrew his insistence on the inclined plane. His dominance over the Canal Commissioners soon faded. De Witt Clinton, so far as the politics and policies of the canal project were concerned, pretty much took Morris' place.

At an extra session of the Legislature in June 1811, Jonas Platt introduced a bill in the State Senate authorizing the Canal Commissioners to buy all of the privately held shares in the Lock Navigation Company, but not until the Legislature had passed an act authorizing the beginning of operations for opening a dug canal. The bill also authorized the

*They developed into the two canal engineers who built the Champlain Canal and the Erie Canal.

Commissioners to accept grants of land which anyone might offer as an aid in furthering the canal project. Lastly, they were empowered to negotiate a loan of five million dollars on the credit of New York State. The bill passed approximately as offered and became a law. In presenting this bill, Platt established a new pattern.

After Clinton and Morris had made a great dramatic effort which had developed into a farce, it became Platt's function to step out from behind a wing where a prompter usually stands, take over the act, and save the show.

CHAPTER TEN

THE DECLINE AND FALL OF DE WITT CLINTON

It soon developed that Governor Tompkins was also watching Clinton. There were certain surface indications, obscure to the public but clear to Tompkins' practiced eye, that Clinton had White House aspirations, and not in the interest of the canal, but for the glorification of De Witt Clinton.

Tompkins was aware that Clinton's first step toward the White House would be to secure the nomination at the Republican caucus of the New York Legislature. Having secured that, Clinton's second step would be to win the presidential nomination at the Republican caucus in Congress. Tompkins owed Clinton a debt of gratitude for his political training, but he could not forget what a whip-cracking, arrogant mule-skinner Clinton had been. Naturally, he did not relish the idea of Clinton, as President of the United States, again riding him.

To thwart Clinton's first step, Tompkins on a pretext dismissed the State Legislature and did not call them back until the Republican caucus in Congress had nominated President Madison to succeed himself.

On May 29, at the Republican caucus of the State Legislature, Clinton did secure the presidential nomination over the protests of Tompkins, Tammany, the Livingstons, Clinton's brother-in-law Ambrose Spencer, Clinton's implacable enemy John Tayler, and a number of unidentified men not interested in seeing their names in the paper.

With the facial expression of one who has drunk vinegar, Clinton set about pleasing everyone for the sake of their votes. He began by calling himself the American Federalist, eloquently sympathizing with the Federalist aversion to a war against England which Madison had declared on June 18, 1812. He promised that if he were elected, he would make peace with England. Naturally, some of the Republicans desiring war with England were offended. To placate them, Clinton denounced Madison for not promoting the War of 1812 more vigorously.

Despite his clumsy efforts to please all of the voters, Clinton received the Federalist nomination for the Presidency and the support of that master politican and manipulator, Martin Van Buren. Clinton made a supreme effort, but Madison, backed by Pennsylvania and the South, defeated him.

Clinton seemed stunned by his defeat. His enemies and some of his former friends, perceiving that he was being glanced at covertly and avoided, tried to kick him still lower. Concomitantly, the canal project was mentioned less and less frequently.

As the war with Canada progressed, due to the impracticability of transporting heavy artillery, ammunition, and military supplies on the inferior turnpikes which crossed New York State, the unsupported American troops at Niagara were routed. The Niagara frontier fell to the British. Then the British took Detroit. There were naval battles on the ocean, on Lakes Erie and Champlain, but strangely no British armament appeared before the Port of New York. A rumor spread in New York City that word of Tompkins' preparations had reached the British, causing them to seek more vulnerable Atlantic ports. Tompkins' preparedness became a fashionable topic of conversation. He was the man of the hour. New Yorkers proudly called him the "War Governor."

Although riding the crest of popularity, Tompkins was mindful that a wave slopes both ways. Clinton seemed to be politically dead. However, the canal project still had some supporters. Therefore, until Tompkins had also eliminated the canal, there would always be the possibility of a Clinton revival. Using the war as his argument, Tompkins contrived on April 15, 1814 to have the canal act rescinded by the Legislature and the Canal Commissioners stripped of all substantial power. This act reduced them to a mere board of consideration. The act passed the Assembly by a large majority and the Senate by a unanimous vote. Clinton described it as "the culmination of a long threatened storm."

On September 26, 1814, when the war was within three months of termination and danger to New York State had passed, Tompkins called a special session of the Legislature. His purpose was to have laws passed creating a State Guard, a Coast Guard, and for the assessment of property to provide a fund for defense. For offense, he devised another law to promote privateering against enemy commerce by forming associations for that purpose.

Despite Tompkins' popularity, his inflammatory speech caused an uproar in both houses of the Legislature. When things had quieted down a bit a vote was called. Although the Federalists voted solidly negative, all of the military acts passed both houses and were sent to the Council of Revision for approval or veto.

According to the provisions of the State Constitution, the Council of Revision consisted of the Chancellor of the State Supreme Court, currently James Kent, the Chief Justice who happened to be John Tayler's protégé, Smith Thompson, and any two associate justices of the State Supreme Court. All four of the associate justices had the privilege of attending a meeting of the Council of Revision and of voting if they so wished. Despite that privilege, precedent had established that only two associate justices attend.

Experience had demonstrated that the attendance of four associate justices contributed only twice the volume of wrangling and bickering without increasing the wisdom of the final decisions. The governor, or the acting governor, was required by law to be present at each Council meeting to cast a vote in the event of a tie.

One of Chancellor Kent's ears seemed still to tingle from the impact of a brick dislodged from that Danbury schoolhouse chimney by a British fieldpiece, when, as a boy, he had watched a Revolutionary skirmish. Boyish aversion had age-ripened into a fixation that no good had or ever would emerge from war or preparation for war. Indeed the preceding December 24 he had written a letter to his brother, Moss Kent, unburdening his heart on the subject of war. The letter included: "The prospect of our affairs is chilling. I see no ground for hope for we can never expect peace so long as men reign over us who have such a deadly malice toward England." But not until his seat in the Council of Revision required his vote on the military measures instigated by Governor Tompkins did Kent have an opportunity by an official act to impede the course of war. Each time during those meetings, when it became his turn to vote, he arose and made a short speech about the futility of war and particularly of the measure under consideration. In a voice of suppressed fury, Kent condemned all military acts as "contrary to the genius of the American Constitution and repugnant to the civilized and enlightened spirit of the age." However Kent's adverse vote was in vain. All of Tompkins' war measures were approved by a majority of the Council of Revision. Kent raised no further protest—but he did not forget. In his letter to his brother one of "the men who reign over us" was Daniel Tompkins, President Madison's able assistant in conducting the War of 1812.

As for Jonas Platt, the Council of Appointment of 1813 gave him a long-deserved Associate Justiceship on the State

Supreme Court Bench. At the same time they somewhat reluctantly continued Clinton as Mayor of New York. For this bit of tolerance Clinton was indebted partly to admiration for his fighting qualities by two Federalist members of the Council but mostly to Tompkins' dread of adverse gossip if he should throw out Clinton, his former sponsor and patron.

Platt discharged with credit his duties as a Supreme Court Justice, gaining steadily in public respect, but soon after October 1814 Clinton lost his job as mayor. He had spent all of his own money and most of his wife's. Discredited, friendless, and hopeless, he withdrew to a farm at Newtown, Long Island, where he drank plenty of cheap whiskey and sulked. De Witt Clinton was down and out.

At last the curtain had fallen on the drama of the canal project. Yet one man remained behind the scenes in the darkness—hoping. While he waited he secretly paid for Clinton's living expenses. He was a gentle unobtrusive man, a Quaker named Thomas Eddy.

* * * * *

Every two or three weeks during the summer of 1815 Thomas Eddy mounted his horse, crossed to Long Island on the ferry, and rode to Newtown to visit the dazed, dishevelled drunk who had been De Witt Clinton. For a gift, Eddy would take Clinton a box of one hundred cigars. To gauge the intensity of Clinton's intoxication, Eddy watched the trembling of Clinton's hands as he lighted one.

During the July visits Eddy had to do all of the talking. Clinton occasionally grunted a reply. His face and neck were flushed. He wanted a fight to ease his resentment toward everyone. By August Clinton's mood became melancholy. He had been "hard done by" and now he wanted to tell Eddy about it. By September, Clinton seemed to have discovered that whiskey would not solve his problem. Consistent with his behavior pattern, he turned away from all liquor.

Eddy's next call was fortunately timed. He found Clinton in a condition of deep reaction due to his abrupt sobriety. Clinton's hands were still shaking. He was pale and jumpy and very sorry for himself.

Eddy suggested that as a remedy Clinton do something, such as making a lecture tour to reawaken interest in the canal project. He gave Clinton his pocketbook and his horse and told him to ride to Buffalo and start back eastward, lecturing at each village on what the lack of adequate transportation had cost New York during the recent war with England. Eddy further explained that although for Clinton a lecture tour would be a menial undertaking, he would have to shut his teeth on that loss of dignity and make a success of his lectures. If he could thoroughly arouse the countryside, he might yet win his way back to power. He must not regard his lectures lightly. They might indeed be his last chance.

For Clinton the "road back" began at Newburgh, the eastern terminus of the Susquehannah and Bath Turnpike. As he rode westward toward the Seneca Turnpike he tried not to visualize bedbugs as big as beans but to focus his attention upon the effects of the war on the various communities. From wayside information and anecdote he built his lecture.

Clinton's first speech was delivered at an open-air meeting in Buffalo where there was no church available in which to assemble his audience. To check the sneezing, coughing, and to silence the general murmur of the gathering he made the astounding statement that if a canal were built, ten years after its completion Buffalo would become the second city in New York State. Since Buffalo, only five years previously, had consisted of forty houses and five lawyers the audience naturally assumed that Clinton either did not know what he was talking about, or was trying to be facetious.

From that low point Clinton's lecture, following the pattern of his personality, became an harangue in which he tried to convince his listeners by a series of arguments that commerce would center in Buffalo because it would tie the budding industry of the east to the vast potential of agriculture in the west. Clinton left them with two admonitions—to vote for the canal and to buy for investment Buffalo real estate.

As Clinton rode eastward he adapted his canal lecture until it became a show. His theme was always the canal, but he somehow included those awful men in the Legislature who had killed the proposed canal measure. That measure had been introduced primarily for the benefit of the communities living in western and central New York. He was smart enough to keep his own efforts out of his lectures, although by inference he let it be understood that he had gone down fighting for their interests like a St. George being licked by a dragon.

Appreciating that people respond favorably to that which they understand, and that they understand best the things which they already know, Clinton recounted the deficiencies of New York State turnpikes, particularly in time of war. He cited for example, a cannon which, sold at an eastern foundry for $200, had cost the government (and the audience was a part of the government) $2,000 for transportation by turnpike to the western frontier. Turnpikes were built for commercial traffic, not for the hundreds of heavily loaded military wagons which cut ever deepening ruts into the soft road surface as thousands of horses hauled them to the theater of war. Nor was there enough fodder along the route for so many horses. Half-starved, the horses struggled to haul creaking wagons through lowland quagmires and up steep hills. Many horses had died. Wagons had to be abandoned. Troops guarding the New York frontier were put on short rations. The cost of delivering a barrel of pork to Fort Niagara had been $126!

If there should be another war with England, and meanwhile no canal had been built, the people of western New York would again be defenseless. But there was no need of such a helpless condition. The money which the government had spent in the recent war on the transportation of military supplies would have built a canal half way across the State! And now the money was gone and the United States had not even won the war. Looking back, anyone could see what should have been done. But would they do it now? Would the State provide that best of all defenses—a canal? The answer was obvious. "Those Albany politicans wouldn't wish to be guilty of anything so progressive!" If that closing remark failed to draw a laugh, Clinton would tell them his favorite funny story: his joke about a mule named Daniel Tompkins which did not believe in building the canal because he thought that he would have to do all the work!

* * * * *

Late in the autumn of 1815, while Jonas Platt was in New York City holding court, Thomas Eddy invited him to breakfast. At an early hour Jonas arrived, expecting to commiserate with his host over the decline of De Witt Clinton and the fall of the canal project.

A Negro butler in livery admitted Jonas and, after taking his hat and cane, conducted him to a carpeted breakfast room lighted by a crystal chandelier and furnished with Duncan Phyfe table and chairs and a fireplace surmounted by an Italian marble mantel and trimmed with brass appointments. The walls were covered with scenic paper. The air was sweet and fresh and spiced with the odor of boiling coffee. Before the fire stood Thomas Eddy, alone. His face was shaven and powdered. He was wearing fawn trousers and a russet-colored velvet morning jacket. He greeted

Jonas with a warm smile, a hearty handshake and a pat on the shoulder. After they were seated, Eddy so manipulated the breakfast conversation that it consisted of an interchange of funny stories and amusing anecdotes. Jonas' impression was that Eddy was leading a life of luxurious ease, requiring no effort more strenuous than entertaining. Secretly it puzzled Jonas how Eddy could enjoy so much leisure and yet find time to amass so much obvious wealth.

Over cigars Jonas confided that he had been feeling despondent because the canal project was dead and its champion had vanished from politics. Eddy smiled knowingly and said that the champion had indeed been routed in the political bull ring. A bit of adversity had been necessary to bring him down to the level of the man in the street. However, Clinton had made a fresh start at Buffalo. Including every community and crossroads, Clinton had lectured his way to New York. Behind him the whole State was in an uproar. Hadn't Jonas heard of it? Jonas hadn't. "But even so," Jonas said, "with a Tompkins-controlled Legislature at Albany hostile to the canal, and with Tammany-controlled New York laughing at it, no one of importance dares listen to anything pertaining to the canal! That big noise from upstate, Thomas, though it may indicate an interest in the canal, can never bring about the passing of a canal law." After reflecting, Jonas continued bitterly that as long as Tompkins was Governor, every spare dollar in the State Treasury would be spent on military preparedness. Jonas added that in view of Tompkins' fantastic popularity, he could not visualize Tompkins as ever going down in defeat.

Eddy grinned tolerantly and suggested that while there was not much chance of Tompkins going down, he might go higher, and that would be just as effective in clearing the way for the canal issue. Meanwhile, Eddy said, the time had come for a revival of the canal project. Something should be done to rally the scattered and dispirited canal supporters

—such as a big dinner at the City Hotel on the evening of December 3 with all of the prominent men in New York invited. William Bayard had already agreed to preside. Clinton would be the guest speaker. Would Jonas make the introductory speech?

Jonas would! On that fateful December evening when Jonas spoke, he included an appeal for public abandonment of the idea of a canal on an inclined plane. John Swartwout followed with an exhortation for a definite "Canal Policy" which set the stage for the speaker of the evening.

De Witt Clinton arose. As if at command the dining hall was silent. Everyone could see that here was a new, a purified-by-ordeal, Clinton. In his resonant voice, speaking with timing and emphasis, Clinton reminded his listeners that the United States had defended its boundaries and had obtained an honorable peace, but that the country was still in dire peril. The treasury was empty. The nation's credit was literally used up. It might still be possible to raise half a million dollars in gold and silver, but only by a most ruinous sacrifice of collateral resources. What the United States needed was not more war, not further preparedness, but trade and commerce. And since the country must have goods to exchange, there had to be a corresponding development of internal resources, treasury, and transportation to forward the products. From south to north through the great Appalachian barrier, there was just one gap at water level. That gap ran across central New York. Within the boundaries of the United States it was the only possible route for transporting the products of the vast interior to the eastern seaboard. If along this route a canal should be built, there would be an awakening, a revival of commerce, an upsurge in industry, and an undreamed-of era of prosperity!

Clinton sat down amid enthusiastic applause. Under cover of the noise Eddy spoke to Platt. Platt passed the word to Bayard. When the room had quieted, Bayard proposed that a committee be appointed to petition the Legislature on behalf of a canal. The committee, having been appointed, as its first act, requested Clinton to write the petition. That petition became known as the New York Memorial. It was signed by an impressive number of prominent New Yorkers, adopted as a model for the drafting of similar memorials by most of the upstate communities, and presented to the convocation of the next Legislature on January 30, 1816. Collectively, the petitions included more than one hundred thousand signatures.

So impetuous was the onrush of the new Canal Policy that the opponents, with no time to organize a countermeasure, had to temporize with a whispering campaign ridiculing the canal proponents. Despite muted whispers and cloaked thrusts, the Canal Policy continued to be more and more the subject of discussions in halls and anterooms.

To dampen interest in the Canal Policy, Governor Tompkins, who believed in carefully feeling his way when setting up opposition, warned the Legislature that it rested with them "to determine whether the canal was sufficiently important to demand the appropriation of some part of the revenue of the State without imposing too great a burden upon our constituents."

The public reaction to this guarded but insinuating speech was an increase in the number of pro-canal mass meetings and another flood of signed petitions. Now fully alarmed, Governor Tompkins focused his attention upon ways of diverting the public mind from the canal. The canal meant Clinton, and the Governor was sure that the people, regardless of what they might think about Clinton, did not understand him and could never be happy with him.

After pondering this, Tompkins concluded that Platt's plea at the canal dinner for the abandonment of the "inclined plane" idea suggested that there might be a fissure in what appeared to be a solid front of the Board of Canal Commissioners who had been holding their office since the Act of April 8, 1811. To bring matters to a head, Tompkins asked them for a report.

The first draft of the report alluded to "The number and respectability of the applications now before the legislature in favor of an immediate commencement and vigorous prosecution of this great national work . . ." but made no mention of the inclined plane, or sailing ships right through from Bristol Harbor to Lake Erie. Nowhere in the report was Gouverneur Morris mentioned, nor did his signature appear with the others. To the public, the absence of the Morris signature was the first surface symptom of that obscure fissure which Governor Daniel Tompkins had already perceived. Hitherto, Morris had been the leader and spokesman for the Canal Commissioners. So high had been his prestige that no Commissioner had dared oppose him.

That the other Commissioners should exhibit their disagreement by writing a report without even consulting him exceeded heresy. It was open revolt. And in Morris' view the more regrettable because they had shown not only a lack of understanding of the subject but had demonstrated that they did not even know how to write a report. That the public might not be deprived by that inadequacy, Morris graciously wrote his own report. In almost anyone's book two reports spelled "fissure."

In the spirit which had prompted the revolt, the other Commissioners attempted to point out to Morris a number of flaws in his report. But Morris, knowing that when a report was perfect it needed no amendment, indignantly refused to alter it. Silenced, but not subdued, the other Commissioners drafted yet another report which they presented to a joint committee of the Senate and Assembly, again without the Morris signature.

To widen the breach, Tompkins encouraged plenty of committee debates and amendments to the submitted report.

The final report emerged from the joint committee in the form of an act to appoint a new Board of Canal Commissioners who were directed to cause the "necessary plans, surveys and estimates to be made." The appropriation to cover the cost of their labors was twenty thousand dollars.

The sleeper in this act was in the personalities of the men selected for the new Board of Commissioners. Some were Federalists and patrician. Others were Republicans and plebian. All were opinionated and stubborn. If, in devising plans for the exact route and estimating the cost of construction, the new commissioners should fail to get into that pitch of arguing which would result in division and stalemate, Tompkins was willing to bet that no two men in New York State would ever argue again. And the expense account was sufficiently large to maintain the Board during a protraction of their arguments until voters all over the State began taking sides. In that event the canal policy would soon be forgotten in the far more fascinating issue of convincing, or at least silencing. Consequently, Tompkins was sure that before anything could be settled he would be in Washington and indifferent to the prospects of either Clinton or the canal.

Tompkins' plan, though excellent for Tompkins, unfortunately reached the hot-under-the-collar stage rather sooner than he had anticipated. Members of the Assembly had received so many insulting letters from their constituents demanding that they be told why nothing was being done about a canal, "or else"—that the act, as passed by the Assembly, provided for the immediate beginning of construction between Rome and the Seneca River. Meanwhile, the canal clique in the Assembly, detecting the possibility of a split in the Board of Canal commissioners, increased their number to thirteen.

When the Assembly-amended act was presented to the Senate, Martin Van Buren, acting in the interest of Governor

Tompkins, struck eight names from the list of Commissioners and every clause authorizing construction. The reason given by Van Buren was that "more accurate knowledge is required before a law authorizing the work can be justified." He let them guess the reason for the deletion of eight names from the list of Commissioners—to get them used to guessing.

When the Senate-amended Act was returned to the Assembly, the Assembly refused to concur in the Senate's amendments and returned it to them. But the Senate refused to recede from its position!

When the act was again returned to the Assembly it was at last obvious to the proponents of the Canal Policy that Governor Tompkins' fine Italian hand was working through his adherents in both Houses of the Legislature. He had first delayed a vote on the act in the Assembly, then hastened the amending in the Senate so that the act when returned to the Assembly, would reach them the last day of the session. This timing allowed no opportunity for a compromise in the provisions of the act through a joint committee of both Houses.

The Canal clique in the Assembly knew that the ordering of another survey to furnish "more accurate knowledge" would serve no purpose, other than to retard the Canal program until Tompkins could divert public attention to his pet project, military preparedness.

On the other hand, if the Assembly should vote nonconcurrence with the Senate version, the act would be dropped until the next session, and perhaps forever. However, should the Assembly accept the Senate amendments, the act though crippled and almost meaningless would remain alive. In another year, under more favorable political conditions an effective act based on this one might succeed.

There was no time for further debate. In the Assembly the whip was cracked. During the last few minutes of the session, the Senate revision of the act containing not a single clause authorizing construction was offered in the Assembly and voted favorably. Having the Tompkins blessing, the act also passed the Senate and the Council of Revision—to become a useless law!

The Canal clique in the Assembly believed afterward that Tompkins had expected them to reject the Senate-amended version and was somewhat thrown off balance by their unexpected acceptance. In that sense they had won a sort of moral victory. And yet, despite that victory, the clique somehow had a feeling that they were still "behind the eight ball."

On November 5, 1816 Governor Tompkins called a special session of the Legislature for the purpose of making "Provision . . . for employing State prisoners either in building a new prison at Auburn . . . repairing roads or constructing canals. . . ." That was what Tompkins said in his opening address, but it soon got around that the Legislature had really been convoked to choose presidential electors.

In the ensuing presidential election Tompkins had hoped to be the Republican nominee for president, but Monroe, backed by the Southerners, was chosen. Tompkins was offered as a consolation the nomination for Vice-President. Although bitterly disappointed at being second choice, Tompkins was somewhat consoled later by being elected Vice-President of the United States. Tompkins could legally have retained his governorship while he was Vice-President, but he resolved to resign his governorship and concentrate on cultivating the southern politicans and hope for better luck at the next presidential nomination. Right there Tompkins made a mistake because his resignation as governor would necessitate the election of a new governor for New York in April 1817 to take office the following July 1. And that would give De Witt Clinton a chance to run for governor.

CHAPTER ELEVEN

THE CANAL LAW

At the convocation of the Legislature on January 14, 1817, Governor Tompkins made a speech asking that a resolution be offered abolishing slavery in New York State, effective July 4, 1827. In the sweetness and tenderness of his voice there was no slightest quaver to suggest his breaking heart because of his "also ran" finish in the recent presidential race. His appeal, pure and liquid, "Not for myself, but for my fellow man I ask it," aroused a profound emotional reaction, not only in the Legislature but, as fast as it could be reported, throughout New York State and even New England.

An abolition resolution was offered in the Legislature, passed and immediately became a law. Jonas Platt, Thomas Eddy, and De Witt Clinton were completely in accord, but they were also aware that the tie binding the United States had been loosened and, if other northern states should follow New York's example, it would be further loosened. As for a bond, such as a canal, to hold the States together, the chances, so far as New York was concerned, were correspondingly diminished. Henceforth, no politican in New York State would dare say "No" to Tompkins, the canal's bitterest enemy.

On February 24, 1817, Tompkins resigned his governorship to assume the duties of Vice-President. According to law, Lieutenant Governor John Tayler became Acting-Governor. For years Tayler had been waiting for an opportunity to dismember Clinton. It looked as if the moment had come when on March 25 at the Republican convention for nominating a candidate to fill Tompkins' vacancy, De Witt Clinton won the nomination in the face of bitter Tammany opposition.

On March 18, 1817, the joint committee of the Assembly and the Senate rendered their conclusions based on the latest report of the Canal Commissioners. Only a handful suspected that if the energy, which was motivating group hatreds, were not diverted from its course of destruction into the channels of construction, such as commerce and industry, the State might suffer a depression. Influenced by that handful, the joint committee recommended the immediate commencement of canal construction between Rome and the Seneca River. The Commissioner considered it wise to undertake only a portion of the canal at first, so that there would be a basis of proof whether the estimates of cost were correct. In the event of no more of the canal being built, that section would open to the public new and valuable communications. The joint committee added to their recommendations a plan of finance which at the request of the committee the Canal Commissioners had devised.

On March 19 an act combining these recommendations was presented to the Assembly. William Duer was the sponsor. The response to his first speech was, "Where are we going to get the money?" That simple question sparked a verbal battle which lasted for three weeks. While innuendo and threats were flying back and forth, and occasionally other things too, George Tibbitts, Senator from Rensselaer County and a member of the joint committee, came up with a plan of finance so obviously workable that arguments against it fell flat. Still, the Tammany Assemblyman would not agree. William Rochester, Wheeler Barnes, and Judge Pendleton, all able speakers, remonstrated in their loudest tones, but in vain.

When all hope seemed lost, Elisha Williams, Assemblyman from Columbia County, had an inspiration which derived from his understanding of the people of New York City. First, he reminded them that all freight moving eastward over the canal to ocean tidewater must be consigned to New York warehouses or be transferred across New York docks to ocean-going vessels. In either case the people of New York would have a percentage of profit in an ever expanding business. The expression of the Tammany man relaxed. Temporarily, he forgot Clinton and begun musing about that golden percentage. Without further objecting the act passed the Assembly by a 64 to 35 vote and was delivered by the Assembly Clerk to the Senate.

In the opinion of the ancient and embittered Assembly Clerk the Senate consisted of twenty-eight crotchety old men, elected because of their reputation for faultfinding. The grand passion of "The Honorable the Senate" was marring with amendments every constructive measure sent to them by the Assembly. Why did they not mend something useful like clothes, fences, or leaky kettles. And why were they always addressed as "Honorable"?

The Bill concerning navigable communications between the great western and northern lakes and the Atlantic Ocean, commonly known as the Canal Act, was no exception. The Senate had read the bill, festooned it with amendments and soon after ten o'clock in the morning of April 15 returned it by their clerk to the Assembly. The Assembly was debating the first bill of the morning, one concerning land recently purchased from the Oneida Indians, when the Senate Clerk laid the Senate-amended Canal Act on the Assembly Speaker's desk. As if he had returned something that the cat had brought in, the clerk walked away with uptilted nose.

From the Senate visitor's gallery three distinguished men watched the Senate Clerk return to his chair below the desk of the Senate President, Philetus Swift. They were Chancellor James Kent, Chief Justice Smith Thompson, and from

Washington, to be in at the death, Vice-President Daniel Tompkins. Their expressions were complacent as if they were confident that the Assembly, because of unfinished business, would not find time to read and finish debating the amended Canal Act. On this, the last day of the session!

Seated near them in the Senate gallery and sharing their opinion, but with far different reactions and facial expressions, were Jonas Platt and De Witt Clinton. The sag of their shoulders and down-curved mouth corners evoked smiles, nods, and nudges from the three distinguished men. Thomas Eddy was also in the gallery, but near the end where he could receive a signal from the Senate Clerk, upon whom he had bestowed a gratuity. Suddenly he lost his grave look in a twisted little smile.

The large luminous eyes of Daniel Tompkins, observing that smile, became less complacent. He directed a questioning look toward Martin Van Buren, seated in the front row of the body of the Senate near the Clerk's desk. Van Buren leaned forward and whispered to the Clerk. The Clerk whispered a reply. Van Buren faced toward Tompkins with an astonished look which he modified with a deprecating wave of his hand as if to say, "Yes, it's the Canal Act, returned by the Assembly, but don't worry. It won't get on the Senate floor for a long time."

Nevertheless, Tompkins seemed uneasy as he settled back in his chair to listen drearily to a prolonged, acrimonious debate on the nine o'clock bill, "An Act relative to musicians in the militia." As one harsh but meaningless speech followed another and the hands of the tall clock beside the platform approached eleven, Tompkins relaxed. Promptly at noon the Senate would be recessed. The afternoon meeting, beginning at four, was always brief, and this was the closing day.

It was after eleven when a vote was taken on the Musician's Act. By that time every Senator knew that the Canal

Act had been returned by the Assembly with marginal notations indicating that the Assembly had concurred with some of the Senate amendments but had declined others.

The moment had come for the Senate to consider the next bill. Mr. Swift suspended his gavel while the Senate settled down. From brief whispers and a certain tension in the faces of the Senators it seemed as if they were expecting the amended Canal Act to be next. Mr. Swift's gavel fell. The Clerk arose and droned that the Honorable, the Senate, would now consider a bill concerned with payments to certain officers of the government therein mentioned.

Van Buren flashed a triumphant smile toward Daniel Tompkins. Tompkins acknowledged with a slight inclination of his head. The canal opponents, becoming exuberant, expressed themselves in a light splatter of clapping. Mr. Swift tapped for order. As the Clerk intoned four amendments to the Act, each of which would consume at least ten minutes of arguing, not to mention the time which would be consumed in taking a vote, several Senators turned in their seats and grinned admiringly at Daniel Tompkins. Jonas Platt and De Witt Clinton wagged their heads, gazing dismally at the floor. By their pantomine they conveyed that there was no hope for the canal, absolutely none.

With a fixed grin of morbid fascination Thomas Eddy cupped an ear, the better to hear the debate about the first amendment. The question was, "Should the annual salaries paid quarterly to the State Governor be as much as six thousand dollars, the Attorney General two thousand dollars, and the Governor's Secretary three hundred dollars?" At the outset it seemed as if discussion of such a subject could never be exhausted, but it soon became apparent that the annual payment of such huge sums of money even to elevated public servants attracted little sympathy.

At 11:14 A.M. the rising volume of coughing and shuffling of feet among the Senators caused Tompkins to whisper in

Smith Thompson's ear. Thompson half arose, but sat down again as Mr. Swift's gavel ended the debate. Votes on three amendments were called in succession. All were negative. The bill was returned to committee and probably to oblivion. Jonas Platt shuddered. If the Senate would not increase the wretched salaries of vital state officers by a few dollars, what chance would there be for the Canal Act with its implied outlay of millions.

The hour hand of the tall clock had reached 11:20 when Mr. Swift rapped in the Canal Act. Jonas gripped the edges of his chair. Clinton's cane tapped a pulsing cadence on the floor. There would not be time now to save the Canal Act, but just having it come up for a third reading caused a stir of consternation among the canal opponents. It showed that they, too, were on edge.

The Senate Clerk had finished the third reading of the Canal Act, but was scarcely seated when Josiah Ogden was on his feet offering a motion that the Canal Act be "recommitted to a committee of the whole for the purpose of amending the bill by expunging or amending the preamble." Ignoring growls at so flagrant a subterfuge, Mr. Swift put the question whether the committee would agree to that motion. The vote was so strongly negative that Daniel Tompkins sat bolt upright and Clinton stopped tapping with his cane.

Mr. Swift then put the pertinent question, "Should the Canal Act, as amended by the Assembly be passed by the Senate?" Again Josiah Ogden was on his feet. He insisted on a roll-call vote. When the vote had been taken, it added up to two-thirds affirmative. By that vote the Senate had now agreed to all of the Assembly's amendments to the Canal Act. But the Assembly had yet to accept those of the Senate, particularly the one which concerned the acquistion by the State of the interests and rights of the defunct Lock Navigation Company.

With a martyred sigh, the Senate Clerk picked up the Canal Act, shrugged and stalked off to the Assembly. Tompkins, Thompson, and Kent watched him go, then turned to each other with understanding smiles. There was not the slightest possibility that the Canal Act could come to a vote in the Assembly before noon. Even if it were returned to the Senate in the afternoon, there would not be time to consider it because of the closing hour. The anti-Canal Act group glanced at each other with satisfaction and nodded. Clinton resumed his tapping.

Then the seemingly impossible happened. The hour hand stood at quarter of twelve. The interim had been crowded with amendments to bills about banks, the laying out of roads, and the bidding of an affectionate farewell to ex-Governor Tompkins. Tompkins was on his feet bowing to the applause when suddenly the decrepit Assembly Clerk came in and handed to the Senate Clerk what everyone knew instinctively to be the Canal Act. Ostensibly, the Assembly just could not decide anything that quickly, and yet there it was.

With his gavel Mr. Swift stopped the applause and ordered the Senate Clerk to read. Arising, the Clerk said that there was nothing to be read except a note from the Assembly that they disagreed with the Senate's insistence upon retention of the fourth amendment, the one pertaining to the Lock Navigation Company.

Jonas Platt, who had been enduring a mounting feeling of futility, at that moment experienced complete frustration. The Assembly had rejected a Senate amendment, one in which a great deal of money was involved and therefore not easily compromised. Time had run out. This was indeed the end. Angrily, Clinton banged the floor with his cane. A few anti-canal Senators had started to clap when suddenly the Senate Chamber became hushed. Martin Van Buren had the floor.

Because of a ringing in Jonas' ears, Van Buren's voice seemed to come from afar. Van Buren was making an impassioned plea for the Canal Act! Baffled, Jonas tried to find an explanation. Evidently Van Buren had felt a change in the direction of the political wind.

Tompkins sat down looking pale and acutely ill. Not even his own adherents paid him any attention. They were all watching Van Buren's show. Van Buren was careful not to talk too long. As he ended his brief but powerful plea he was greeted with thunderous applause. Mr. Swift's gavel rapped. At a glance from Van Buren, Mr. Cochran sprang to his feet to claim the floor. Speaking quickly, he moved that the Senate recede from its fourth amendment of the Canal Act. Instantly several red-faced men sprang to their feet shouting arguments, but Mr. Ditmis got in just one shout ahead of them, demanding a roll-call vote. The result was thirteen affirmatives to twelve negatives. By a majority of one vote the Senate receded from the fourth amendment and returned the Canal Act to the Assembly. Both Houses having now reached complete agreement on the Canal Act, the Assembly without further ado passed it along to the Council of Revision, promptly notifying Mr. Swift of their action.

The tall clock had struck noon. The Senate was noisily dispersing when the Governor's Secretary hurried in, shouldered his way through the confusion and handed Mr. Swift a message. Mr. Swift glanced at the message, rapped sharply and announced that Acting-Governor Tayler had requested the Council of Revision to meet promptly at one o'clock.

De Witt Clinton, who had started to pat Jonas on the back, abruptly stopped patting. In Jonas' ear he mumbled, "James Kent and Smith Thompson are against us. You and Joe Yates will make a tie in the Revision vote. Tayler will have a casting vote. He sent Justices Van Ness and Spencer out on circuit to get them out of Albany. He knew that if they were here, they'd turn the tables. But one o'clock! Why they couldn't fly here by that time if they had wings. In the moment of victory we are destroyed. Now there will never be a canal." He took Jonas by the arm, "Well, let's go and get some dinner."

Jonas shook him off. "No, I can't eat. I must think. I'm going to stay right here until one o'clock and think this thing through. There must be some way out. I'm sure there is. If only I can think of it. But there's so little time——."

For the next forty-six minutes Jonas, feeling as if he were treading a very high tight-rope, paced the empty corridor in mental turmoil. As the chimes of the tall clock boomed one note of doom, Jonas, having watched all of the other members arrive, entered the Council of Revision Chamber with bowed head.

Only once previously had Jonas seen John Tayler smile, and that had been when Tayler was watching Solomon Van Rensselaer being caned. Now Tayler was downright affable. By his manner he showed that he had waited a long time for the pleasure of this moment.

It occurred to Jonas that perhaps Tayler might be persuaded to delay a few minutes. In the empty darkness of Jonas' mind a spark had been struck. It grew rapidly into a tiny glow of hope. Somewhere in the Capitol Daniel Tompkins must surely be waiting to hear the decision of the Council. Why had Tompkins resigned his governorship on February 24? Had he forseen the possibility of this meeting and planned to escape the stigma of casting the decisive negative against an act which had behind it such widespread public approval? Surely he would not have left Washington with Congress still in session and come to Albany to be present at the last day of the Legislative session unless he had felt quite certain that the Canal Act would come to a vote. Had he anticipated some flaw in Tayler's plan and wished to be present to lend a guiding hand if necessary? With Thompson and Kent solidly against the canal and Tayler holding a casting vote, veto of the Canal Act should not take longer than fifteen minutes. After fifteen minutes Tompkins would become uneasy. If the veto could be delayed for half an hour Tompkins might poke his pontifical head in at the door to find out what was holding up the decision. That would be Jonas' chance. It was a faint hope, but the only one.

While Jonas had been thinking, Tayler had called the meeting to order and had presented the proposition. Jonas promptly requested that the Act be read from beginning to end, and that a reasonable time be allowed thereafter for discussion, before taking a vote. Acting-Governor Tayler, unconcerned with Daniel Tompkins' trepidation, was unable to see any reason for denying himself the pleasure of watching Platt and Yates writhe a bit longer. Since that was their wish, Tayler readily agreed.

After the Act had been read, Tayler turned to bulldog-faced Chancellor Kent, the senior Justice, and asked for his opinion. Speaking honestly and sincerely, Kent said that he considered it a gigantic project which would require the wealth of all the United States to accomplish; that it had passed the Legislature by small majorities only after a desperate struggle and that he thought it inexpedient to commit the State to such a vast undertaking until public opinion could be better united in its favor.

To Jonas it seemed as if a voice from the past was speaking. He had not been present at that meeting of the Council of Revision in September of 1814 when Governor Tompkins' Defense and Privateering Act had been considered, but Kent in the bitterest of tones had told him the story. Kent and another Federalist Associate Justice had voted against Tompkins' war measure. Smith Thompson, who was controlled by Tompkins and Tayler and the third Associate

Justice, had voted favorably. To break the resulting tie Tompkins had exercised his casting vote and the act had become a law. And now, at this meeting of the Council, the line-up was similar except that Kent was on Tompkins' side instead of in opposition. But if this Act were pertaining to war instead of a peaceful canal, how would Kent vote? Perhaps if Tompkins should come and start talking about war, Kent might change his mind.

Meanwhile, Smith Thompson, next in rank, was speaking with disarming frankness. He said that he cherished no hostility toward the canal and that he would not inquire as to the majorities. Since the Legislature had agreed to the measure, he would be inclined to leave the responsibility with them. But the Act gave arbitrary powers to the Commissioners over private rights without proper guards, and he was therefore opposed to the bill.

Yates and Platt declared themselves in favor. Tayler "panted with honest zeal to strangle the infant Hercules at birth by casting his vote in the negative." So there the Council stood, two and two, with Tayler about to use his casting vote. Tayler raised his gavel. Jonas shouted in remonstrance that neither he nor Yates had had an opportunity to say a word. Tayler lowered the gavel, scowled and said impatiently, "Very well, say what you have to say," adding with a grin, "not that it will make much difference."

Jonas talked rapidly and, as it seemed to him, without meaning. More than a half hour had passed Tompkins had not come. Inwardly, Jonas was in a panic. From the amused look on Tayler's face Jonas was convinced that he was again betraying himself. Yet he talked on, hoping and listening for a certain footstep out in the hall. Then his throat went dry. No water had been provided. Jonas whispered a few words, clapped a hand over his mouth, and looked with pleading eyes at Yates.

Yates nodded, cleared his throat and in a deep low voice

outlined the importance of the proposed canal to New York and to the United States, both currently and in the future. So lucidly did Yates analyze the various aspects of the Act, and so convincingly did he explain away the objections previously raised that both Chancellor Kent and Chief Justice Thompson were obviously impressed.

Acting-Governor Tayler was also impressed, but in a different way. Irritably, he broke in on Yates, insisting that the discussion had gone far enough and that now it was time to take a vote. Down came the gavel, ending further discussion. For almost two hours Jonas Platt and Joseph Yates had filibustered. Tompkins had not come. Now it was too late. Despairing Jonas turned toward the door.

There had been no footstep in the hall. The door merely opened and there stood Tompkins as though he had been outside all of the time listening and having gained the impression that Kent was wavering, and perhaps Thompson as well, had entered to undo Yates' persuasiveness.

Tompkins had neither a constitutional nor legal right to enter that Chamber while the Council was in session, but Tompkins had become a privileged character in New York State. Apparently, he could do as he pleased wherever he pleased and, as he stood looking down into the uncompromising eyes of James Kent his autocratic manner suggested, to whomever he pleased. Tayler, who had become decidedly uneasy, was unaffectedly glad to see Tompkins and asked him to sit down. Jonas' impression that Tompkins had been listening was heightened when, ignoring the others, Tompkins focused his attention on Kent as if he were convinced that Kent had wavered in his opposition to the Canal.

With the condescending patience of a Vice-President of the United States explaining a recondite point to a mere Chancellor of a State Supreme Court, Tompkins called to Kent's attention that the late peace with Great Britain was a mere truce; that we would undoubtedly soon have a renewal of war with that country, and that instead of wasting the credit and resources of the State on this chimerical canal project, the State should immediately employ all of its revenue and credit in providing arsenals, arming the militia, erecting fortifications, and preparing for war.

Watching Kent, Jonas could read his reaction in his face. That faint spark in the darkness of Jonas' mind suddenly burst into a white light. In 1814, Kent had not retorted because it would not have done any good. Now it would. With flashing eyes and suppressed voice Kent asked, "Do you think so, sir?"

Seeming to believe that he had convinced Kent, Tompkins drove home his point. "Yes sir. England will never forgive us for our victories on the land, ocean, and lakes. And my word for it, we shall have another war with her within two years."

Chancellor Kent stood up. His faced was livid. For such a small man he had a very loud voice when he wished to use it. Pounding on the table with both fists and glaring at Tompkins he roared, "If we are to have war, or to have a canal, I am in favor of the canal and I vote for the bill."

The gavel having already fallen, Kent as Chancellor had the privilege of voting first, and indeed had done so.

Smith Thompson voted "No." Platt and Yates, voting affirmatively, outvoted Thompson. There was no tie. Therefore, Tayler could not vote. The Canal Act with provision for immediate construction at that instant became the Canal Law.

Jonas Platt and Joseph Yates looked at each other stunned, arose and quietly left the Chamber. As they walked hurriedly down the corridor, they heard behind them diminutive Kent ably defending himself against the rebukes of Acting-Governor Tayler and Vice-President Tompkins.

* * * * *

At sunrise on July 4, 1817, while the sows in the big swamp two miles south of Rome were teaching their young that through infinite patience succulent frogs could be caught, a large crowd gathered in an adjacent black-soil field. Governor De Witt Clinton, man of the people, in beaver hat, shirt-sleeves, and cigar, was about to plow the first furrow in the excavation of the Erie Canal! Beside the Governor, hitched to a plow, drooped a mule.

From the expressions on the faces in the crowd, the Governor was expected to make a few remarks. Naturally, he could not find it in his heart to disappoint them. He began his speech in his oldtime hortatory tone. Briefly, he sketched the hopeless struggle of the devoted band of canal supporters against the unbelieving, the indifferent, the reactionary. Repeatedly, they had failed. But for twenty-five years, persuaded that the fate of the United States depended upon a canal to bind the west to the east with the bonds of commerce, those dedicated men had never lost faith.

Dropping his voice to a low pleading tone, he entreated his listeners to remember that although the Canal Law had been passed, an even greater struggle lay ahead, the building of the canal. There were hills to be cut through, valleys and rivers to be bridged somehow. Nobody knew how. Worst of all were the broad, bottomless swamps which could be neither filled nor bridged. Also there would be the difficulty of supplying money from a State Treasury depleted by the demands of the recent war.

However, as Gouverneur Moris had said, "Labor improbus omnia vincit."* All of the difficulties might be overcome if only the men of New York State could learn to work together in a great, harmonious effort. But to cooperate in so great an undertaking—and here the Governor's voice dropped to a passionate whisper—they must first cleanse their hearts.

*Labor conquers all.

of grudges and malice. They must learn to forgive and forget and no longer carry hatred in their hearts. There he ended amid hearty applause—although in his heart he continued his speech.

Governor Clinton turned dramatically to the mule. In his thoughts he said "Daniel—Daniel Tompkins! You have not intentionally done anything to make the Erie Canal possible. You would have blocked it if you could. Now at last I am holding the reins and, by the irony of fate, you of all mules are to have the honor of beginning the construction of the Canal, whether you like it or not. This time, Daniel, it's not for you to say. So, giddap, you --- of a -----!"

SELECTED READING LIST

The Official Reports of the Canal Commissioners of the State of New York and the Acts of the Legislature Respecting Navigable Communications Between the Great Western and Northern Lakes and the Atlantic Ocean, B. F. Lewis and Sheldon & Kensett, Newburgh, August 1817.

WHITFORD, N. E. *History of the Canal System of the State of New York,* Supplement to the Annual Report of the State Engineer and Land Surveyor of the State of New York, for the Fiscal Year Ending September 30, 1905, Brandow Printing Company, Albany, 1906.

KIMBALL, FRANCIS P. *New York, the Canal State,* Argus Press, Albany, N. Y., 1937.

JOHNSON, W. FLETCHER and SMITH, RAY B. *Political and Governmental History of the State of New York,* Vol. I (1776-1822), The Syracuse Press, Inc., Syracuse, N. Y., 1922.

HAMMOND, JABEZ. *The History of Political Parties in the State of New York, from the Ratification of the Federal Constitution to December, 1840,* H. & E. Phinney, Cooperstown, N. Y., 1844.

FOX, DIXON RYAN. *The Decline of the Aristocracy in the Politics of New York,* Columbia University, Longmans Green, New York, 1919.

MCBAIN, HOWARD LEE. *De Witt Clinton and the Origin of the Spoils System in New York,* Columbia University Press, New York, 1907.

WATSON, ELKANAH. *History of the Rise, Progress and Existing Condition of the Western Canals in the State of New York,* D. Steele, Albany, N. Y., 1820.

CLINTON, DE WITT. *Remarks on the Proposed Canal from Lake Erie to the Hudson River,* by Atticus (pseud.), Samuel Wood & Sons, New York, 1816.

O'CALLAGHAN, E. B. (Ed.). *Documentary History of the State of New York,* Vol. III–FOR: "Report of a Committee Appointed to Explore the Western Waters of the State: for the Purpose of Prosecuting the Inland Lock Navigation," Western Inland Lock Navigation Company, Barber and Southwick, Albany, N. Y., 1792.

GEDDES, GEORGE. *Origin and History of the Measures that Led to the Construction of the Erie Canal,* Summers & Co., Syracuse, N. Y., 1866 (a pamphlet written at the request of the Buffalo Historical Society).

WRIGHT, BENJAMIN H. *Origin of the Erie Canal: Services of Benjamin Wright,* Sanford & Carr, Rome, N. Y., 1870 (originally published in the *New York Observer,* 1866).

HEDRICK, U. P. *A History of Agriculture in the State of New York* (published by the State), Albany, N. Y., 1933.

JONES, POMROY. *Annals and Recollections of Oneida County,* privately printed in Rome, N. Y., 1851.

CAMPBELL, WILLIAM W. *The Life and Writings of De Witt Clinton,* Baker & Scribner, New York, 1849 (includes Clinton's private Canal Journal of 1810, and other writings on internal improvements).

HOSACK, DAVID. *Memoir of De Witt Clinton,* printed by J. Seymour, New York, 1829,

KNAPP, SAMUEL LORENZO. *The Life of Thomas Eddy,* Conner and Cooke, New York, 1834.

KENT, WILLIAM. *Memoirs and Letters of James Kent* (by his great grandson), Little Brown & Co., Boston, 1898.

DUER, JOHN. *A Discourse on the Life, Character and Public Service of James Kent. . . ,* Appleton, New York, 1848.

State of New York. *The Public Papers of Governor Daniel D. Tompkins,* Vols. I-III (the Military Papers), with a foreword by Hugh Hastings, State Historian, Albany and New York City, 1898-1902.

General Sources

New York State Legislative Documents: Journals of the Senate and Assembly, 1817.

New York State Legislative Manuals.

Constitution of the State of New York.

Dictionary of American Biography.

National Biographical Dictionary.

Special Sources

Private letters from the descendants of Jonas Platt.

CANADA

LAKE ONTARIO

ROCHESTER

BUFFALO

LAKE ERIE

CANANDAIGUA L.

CROOKED L.

SENECA L.

ERIE CANAL

1886

D.K. Negus